Expanding Worlds

IN THIS engrossing work, a leading astronomer presents a comprehensive and easily understood explanation of the recurring evolution of the universe.

Ernst Öpik studies the development of planets, stars, comets and meteors, including much of his own research findings on stellar structure (in particular, his own interpretation of the ice ages); on collisions between celestial bodies; on double stars; on planetary surfaces and atmospheres, as well as the old and new theories of other eminent astronomers and physicists.

Professor Öpik then analyzes the fascinating theory of the oscillating universe: How the universe has expanded to its present status . . . how it will continue to expand until it begins to collapse, melting and disappearing multimillions of years from now . . . how it will reappear in new expansions, new worlds, new metamorphoses.

Other MENTOR Books of Special Interest

One Two Three . . . Infinity *by George Gamow*
Current facts and speculations of science presented
by a leading physicist.   (#MD97—50¢)

New Handbook of the Heavens *by Hubert J. Bern-
hard, Dorothy A. Bennett* and *Hugh S. Rice*
A guide to the stars and planets. (#MD114—50¢)

The ABC of Relativity *by Bertrand Russell*
A clear, penetrating explanation of Einstein's theories and its effect on the world. (#MD258—50¢)

Frontiers of Astronomy *by Fred Hoyle*
An assessment of the remarkable increase in our
knowledge of the universe.   (#MD200—50¢)

THE
Oscillating
Universe

by ERNST J. ÖPIK

A MENTOR BOOK

Published by THE NEW AMERICAN LIBRARY

Foreword

This collection of short essays is written for the unprepared thinking reader as an introduction to our cosmic surroundings. Each chapter is presented as a self-consistent lecture which can be read independently of the rest. The cosmos is here pictured, so to say, in human perspective, the earth with its nearest neighbors being given more attention than the farther portions of the universe.

Particular emphasis is laid on our relation to the cosmos. Unnecessary detail not needed for the general picture is avoided. Although not a course in astronomy, this book is supposed to give a balanced account of the relevant astronomical facts as viewed in the above-mentioned perspective.

The author has had research experience in almost all the topics covered by these essays. His opinions are the outcome of experience and critical study and are not a repetition of textbook maxims. In most cases these opinions will correspond to the generally accepted, up-to-date state of our knowledge. In a few cases they are the author's own original ideas, which, although published, are not yet universally accepted.

Within the limited scope of this book it is not possible to give a full account of different theories and views. The author has chosen instead a subjective method of presentation, the topics being welded together by his own scientific reasoning and philosophy. All his original viewpoints may not pass to posterity, but he will consider his purpose fulfilled if his efforts inspire others in the search for truth, or make them feel the beauty of the cosmos and the mystery of our existence.

ARMAGH, NORTHERN IRELAND

March 31, 1956

The text has been revised after three and a half years since its completion. Only very minor alterations had to be made, in view of the general nature of the contents.

COLLEGE PARK, MARYLAND

October 26, 1959

Contents

1. The Earth among the Stars

THE EARTH AS OUR ABODE OF LIFE HAS IMPRESSED IT-self upon our mind so much that in everyday life we treat it as our universe. When we refer to "the world," we mean the earth, forgetting that our planet is only a tiny speck in the world of planets, suns, and galaxies.

In itself, the smallness of the earth is no reason for denying its importance. One should not be impressed too much by mere quantity; great dimensions and heavy mass have no merit by themselves; they cannot compare in value with immaterial things, such as thoughts, emoti... and other expressions of the soul. To us the ear... most important of all celestial bodies, because it... come the cradle and seat of our spiritual values. Y... the same time, we should be able to assess its place... the material world in correct perspective.

In antiquity, judging naively by appearance, man saw in heaven and earth two equal parts of the material cosmos. Many advanced brains were able to perceive the falseness of this judgment, but they could not, or dared not, insist upon their true views against public opinion; they preferred to teach officially what people wanted to be taught. Passages in the Bible which, if taken literally, are in conflict with modern science, probably originated under pressure, or as the expression of naive public opinion. Saint Augustine, in the fifth century, evidently referred to this when he wrote: "The Lord did not say 'I send you the Spirit [Holy Ghost], to instruct you about the courses of Sun and Moon'; He wanted you to become Christians, not astronomers." Similarly, in the thirteenth century, Thomas Aquinas pointed out that, in questions of the natural sciences, one should not subject the Bible to a crucial test; even if it could be clearly shown that statements in the Bible were scientifically in-correct, one should not proclaim this, "lest the Holy Scripture should be ridiculed by the Unfaithful and, thus, their way to Faith blocked."

In our modern age we have overcome this impediment; we can freely proclaim our scientific findings without endangering spiritual truths.

The most important scientific revelation since Copernican times is the recognition of the fact that the earth belongs to the heavens, being part of them. Instead of using the ancient antithesis between heaven and earth, by which undue material importance was attributed to our planet, we would now say—*the heavens,* including that tiny corner of them which we inhabit and call earth. To us the earth has become a celestial body, one among numberless others.

The earth is a rocky globe, freely suspended in space and moving around the sun. It is kept in its position relative to the sun by the gravitational force of the sun's traction; gravitation counteracts the centrifugal force f orbital motion. The two forces are in equilibrium, and the earth swings around the sun on its annual course—a slightly elliptical orbit. The earth can stay on this orbit for thousands of millions of years to come, as it has done for similar intervals of time in the past. This means that the orbit of the earth is practically stable, or that our planet will not go away far enough from, or come near enough to, the sun to endanger terrestrial life. This stable position of the earth, as well as of its sister planets, depends upon a peculiar feature of the solar system: The central body, the sun, is almost 1,000 times more massive than all its planets taken together; it therefore rules supreme, preventing the planets from considerably disturbing one another's motions. In a system in which the planets are large as compared with their sun, or in which there are several suns, the mutual gravitation of the members of the system plays havoc with the orbits, which change within all imaginable limits. Were our earth a member of such a system—there are numerous such cases among the stars—life could hardly develop on its surface, as it would be extinguished by either heat or cold every time it started.

Thus, happily, the solar system is a monarchy where the earth—a tiny subject—enjoys security, being made to move on its prescribed, almost fixed, path.

Although small among other celestial bodies, by human standards the earth is a body of enormous size. Yet its

dimensions are within the reach of unaided human loco-
motion: it would take only 7,000 hours to walk "around
the world," and many a postman has covered a several
times greater distance during his lifetime. The mass of
the earth is 6,000,000,000,000,000,000,000 tons, a figure
which transcends our powers of imagination. Yet the sun
is 333,000 times heavier, and its circumference is 109
times greater than that of the earth. No wonder it keeps
the earth in obedience from a distance of 93 million
miles, although these millions upon millions of tons of
our globe are racing along with a speed of 18 miles per
second.

If, by some magic, we could detach ourselves from the
earth and stop in space (remaining at rest relative to
the sun) on an evening, we would see the surface of the
earth moving away downwards with terrific speed. Within half a minute we would be well outside the atmosphere,
the terrestrial globe appearing half illuminated, half in
darkness, and still covering the greater portion of a hemisphere. The apparent size of the earth would shrink
quickly, like a railway train racing away. Soon the earth
would assume the appearance of a half-moon, of a beautiful bluish glare, covered with brilliant white spots—clouds
illuminated by the sun—and darker areas where clouds
are absent and the continents and oceans are visible
through the atmospheric haze. Although similar to the
view presented to us by the moon at first quarter, the
spectacle of the earth as seen from space would be much
more colorful and glamorous. As the distance increased,
fewer details on the surface of the earth would be discern-
ible, and the moon (if not already visible) would emerge
from behind the shrinking edge of the earth. After 4
hours we would enjoy the sight of the twin planet earth-
moon, the moon about the same size as it appears to us
now, the earth 3½ times bigger and 60 times brighter
than the moon. While they continued to be carried away
in their orbital motion, their apparent sizes and mutual
distance would seem to decrease. Within a fortnight the
eye would no longer discern the shape or dimensions of
these bodies; they would look like two sparkling points
—a double star of extreme brilliance: the earth in brightness exceeding Venus, the moon equal to Sirius and at
an apparent distance of about half a degree from the

earth (equal to the apparent diameter of the moon for a terrestrial observer). In the background, the black sky of interplanetary space would be studded with numberless stars no longer mindful of the presence of the sun; the sun would be shining in another corner of the sky with undiminished brilliance, yet its rays, not being reflected by an atmosphere, would not interfere with the visibility of the stars.

From our extraterrestrial vantage point the smallness of the earth, as compared with the sun, becomes obvious. The earth looks like a little star beside the giant sun. The comparison, of course, is somewhat misleading. The fixed stars (not planets), although they appear small to us, are not so small at all; they are themselves suns, many of them bigger than ours. Being millions of times farther away than the sun, they look deceptively faint. The 572 million miles which represent the annual path of the earth around the sun encompass a corner of space which is as small compared to stellar distances as the dimensions of a little town are in comparison with those of the solar system.

To take a bird's-eye view of the sun and its planets, let us speed up 10,000 times and travel at 186,000 miles a second, the velocity of light—the greatest velocity attainable by a material object according to relativity. At such a speed we could go 7½ times around the earth in one second, and reach the moon in 1¼ seconds. The distance from earth to sun would be covered in 8 minutes. Let us depart at right angles to the plane of the earth's orbit, or the ecliptic. After one hour's flight the earth will appear as a first-magnitude star, only 8° from the sun—so close that the distance sun-to-earth can be covered by the palm of the outstretched hand; the other planets will be seen at their appropriate distances: Venus and Mercury close to the sun and hardly visible, Jupiter at a distance of 45° from the sun and almost as bright as we see it from earth. After 2 to 3 hours of flight, the earth will become invisible to the naked eye; after 5 days it will no longer be seen in a telescope. Yet, to reach another star—another sun—we should have to travel for 5 years at this speed. The distance attained would then be 5 light years—5 years of travel with the velocity of light. If the solar system were observed from such a distance, nothing but the sun itself, as a star of first magnitude, would be observable with the most powerful human means. To see the earth from a nearby star, or, which is the same, to observe planets of this star from earth, telescopes one mile across and ten miles long would be required: clearly, this appears to be impossible by present human standards. Thus, from the interstellar viewpoint, the earth is nonobservable, or, for all practical purposes, nonexistent. Looking at the starry sky, we have to overlook the planets; it is suns alone that count now, our sun—a brilliant speck embodying the entire solar system—simply one among millions. Yet, to our mental eye, planets, other earths, are ever present in the universe, although physically we cannot see them.

Through its master, the sun, our earth is made a member of the stellar universe. With respect to the swarm of stars in our neighborhood (within a distance of a few hundred light years) our sun is moving with a velocity of 12 miles per second towards a point between the constellations Hercules and Lyra, carrying along all its planets, including the earth. Thus, our globe spirals in interstellar space on a screw-line produced by the combination of the earth's orbital motion around the sun and the translational motion of the solar system towards Hercules-Lyra. With the translational motion it would take some 60,000 years for the sun to cover the distance to the nearest star; on the interstellar scale it is a relatively slow and unimportant motion. Other stars are moving in different directions, without much regularity in their motions. These small relative motions of the millions of stars in our neighborhood remind us of a swarm of dancing gnats.

Yet, by way of the sun, our earth has other loyalties to obey. The swarm of stars which presents itself to us at night, and to which our sun belongs, is not as structureless as it appeared to the astronomers of half a century ago, to whom only the irregular gnat-dance relative motions of its members were known. All these stars belong to a major system, the Milky Way. This galactic system has a flattened shape, like a lens; it contains about 100,000 million stars, about 50 times the human population of the earth, each star either a planetary system or a system of two or more suns (double or multiple stars). It is over 100,000 light years across and thousands of light years thick. Along its equator there are so many stars seen in the same direction that their combined light appears to us as the Milky Way belt. This system is rotating around a center with great speed; the velocity of rotation which carries the swarm of surrounding stars (including our sun) around the center is 150 miles per second. Our sun is at a distance of 28,000 light years from the center of the Milky Way, and it would take us 250 million years to complete one revolution. Unlike the solar system, the Milky Way has no central governing body; it is a republic where the motions of single members are ruled by the combined attraction of the entire population.

Yet the Milky Way, or the Galaxy, is not the only system of its kind in space: there are millions and millions of them in all directions, at distances of millions and hundreds of millions of light years. The earth, through our sun, belongs to one of them, our Milky Way.

The contemplation of the above-described systems, or steps, into which our universe is organized, and to which the earth belongs, may give an idea of the material insignificance of our globe and of the vastness of the universe. At the same time, we may feel elated at being able to grasp the magnificence of the world by our minds —we, tiny creatures on a tiny globe, nay, we, citizens of the heavens through our earth, a celestial body among the stars.

2. The Origin of the Earth

THE ORIGIN OF THE CELESTIAL BODIES IS AS FASCINATING a problem as it is a difficult one. We know only the present state of a small portion of the universe; yet from this limited amount of knowledge we are trying to reconstruct the past history of the whole, in much the same manner as from the outward appearance, the general expression and wrinkles of the face of a stranger, we might try to decipher his life history and origin. The task seems to be almost hopeless.

With respect to the origin of the earth we are much more on solid ground (literally and figuratively speaking) than in the case of other, distant celestial bodies. The study of the rocky surface layers tells us something about the past history of our planet; this is the task of geology, which, among other things, is concerned with the deciphering of fossil remains of past life found in the rock strata. Other sciences—geophysics, seismology, astronomy—help in disclosing the present structure of our globe. The chemist and physicist, by studying radioactivity, are able to tell the age of the rocks, thus putting terrestrial chronology on a solid basis. This, perhaps, is the most spectacular modern achievement in the study of the history of the earth. Radioactive elements slowly change into other, stable elements; thus, uranium and thorium are, in the course of time, converted into certain kinds (isotopes) of lead. The amount of uranium decreases, that of lead increases, gradually. From the relative amounts of these two elements, uranium as the original substance and lead as its end product, one can calculate the age of the rocks which contain them.

Of course, more recent stages in the history of the earth are better known than the earlier ones. The fossil remains found in rocks are subjected to erosion and volcanic activity; the older they are, the more likely they are to have changed or become completely erased.

Our knowledge of the history of the earth's surface for the last 500 million years is relatively complete, whereas for the earlier period of 2,000 to 3,000 million years the data are rather scanty. This is due not only to the difference in age and the loss of old "records," but also to the circumstance that in more recent times fossils were much more numerous and durable. Animals with hard crusts or shells appeared on earth only about 500 million years ago, and these were much better preserved as fossils than their soft predecessors. Therefore, although there was life on earth long before then, few remains of it are found from ages earlier than 500 million years ago.

The oldest rocks so far explored belong to the continent of Africa; their age is about 2,900 million years. A comparative study of the radioactivity of rocks of different ages and origin leads to the conclusion that the earth's solid crust itself is not much older than 3,500 million years. At this remote epoch the beginnings of our globe must be looked for.

It is believed that the earth condensed out of a nebula —a cloud composed of gas and dust—almost simultaneously with the other members of the solar system, the sun and the planets. The dust contained in the solar nebula obscured completely the sun's radiation in the plane of the ecliptic. Except in the nearest surroundings of the sun, it became terribly cold there, perhaps 260 degrees below zero centigrade ($-260°C$). At this low temperature various gases, such as water vapor, ammonia, nitrogen, carbon dioxide, carbon monoxide, and methane, formed "snow flakes" or "icicles" around the dust particles. This cosmic snow began to accumulate into larger pieces, and from the mutual collision of these pieces or "planetesimals" the earth was built. As the earth was growing, its gravitational force increased, and the planetesimals were soon falling on it with velocities sufficient to generate a considerable amount of heat. The growing earth became hot, the icy stuff melted, evaporated, and was lost back to space, whereas the stony or metallic substance remained. This explains why there is so much rock and so little gas on earth, although the nebulae of interstellar space contain 100 times more gas than rocky substance or dust.

Opinions have been expressed that the earth, in the process of formation, although it warmed up considerably, never got hot enough to become completely molten. These opinions were based on the calculation of radiation losses of heat to space from the surface of the earth. However, in these calculations the shielding effect of dust has never been taken into account. The dust filling the space around the growing earth would act as an extremely efficient blanket, preventing heat losses to space, and allowing the surface of the earth (as well as its interior) to become completely molten. There can be little doubt that the earth was liquid at this first, although short, stage of its life. This stage may have lasted "only" about one million years.

The stony material probably separated from metallic nickel-iron while it was in the form of dust in the solar nebula. In the molten earth these substances did not mix permanently: Stony lava, like oil on water, rose to the surface and later became the crust of the earth (when sufficiently cooled); molten iron sank to the bottom forming the earth's core, which is still molten.

The space around the earth was soon (within about one million years) swept clean of dust by the earth itself; the other planets did their share in cleaning up their own surroundings. For the first time the rays of the sun burst through the darkness and shone on our young, still glowing globe. The protective blanket of dust disappeared, and the surface of the earth began cooling quickly. A thin skin of lighter minerals, which now is known as the granitic-basaltic layer, solidified at the surface, but the chief solidification of the earth's crust began at the bottom, 1,800 miles beneath the surface, at the boundary of the molten iron core. At this depth the pressure, over one million atmospheres, is so great that rocks would solidify at temperatures over 4,000°C, while iron could remain molten.

In meteorites, which are broken-off fragments of ancient planets destroyed by collisions, stone is separated from iron, as is believed to be the case in the earth's interior. Radioactive analysis of meteorites, as compared with a similar analysis of the earth's crust, indicates an age of 4,500 million years for the time of separation of iron from stone. This figure is of a good degree of precision; only, we cannot tell for certain to what stage of the evolution of the solar system it refers. Most probably it is the time which just preceded the formation of the earth and other planets. Hence, the over-all age of the earth is 4,500 million years, or somewhat less. This is in good accord with the estimate of not less than 3,500 million years for the age of the solid crust. The solidification of the crust, protected on the outside by the granitic-basaltic skin, may indeed have taken a long interval of time, say 1,000 million years. The cooling must have been slow in the beginning, because of heat generated in the interior by large quantities of radioactive materials (especially radioactive potassium). These materials were only gradually used up, or transported to their present location near the surface of the earth, whence their heat is more readily lost to space and does not much affect the interior.

Not so long ago it was believed that the planets were formed from splashes of solar material, caused by the tidal action of some star that happened to pass near the sun. This theory, still upheld in many textbooks and encyclopedias, has lost ground. The splashes, consisting of extremely hot gas, could not possibly have condensed into the planets; they would have "exploded" into space, becoming a thin gas spread over a large volume without any chance of condensation. On the contrary, the old nebular theory of the origin of the solar system is now gaining support from all sides, after having been in abeyance for half a century.

3. The Origins of Life on Earth

THERE HAVE BEEN MANY SPECULATIONS ON THE POSSIbility of life on other worlds. In this connection, of especial interest is the question how and when life started on our own planet. The "how" remains unanswered at present, the various hypotheses already put forward being still without much support from positive knowledge. With respect to the "when," however, some positive data seem to exist. It is now beyond doubt that highly organized forms of life existed long before the Cambrian period, 500 million years ago, as the Cambrian fossil remains of marine organisms represent an already far-progressed stage of evolution. There is very scanty direct proof of life for earlier epochs. Some geologic data referring to the chemical conditions at which sedimental rocks were formed indicate that about 1,100 million years ago the earth's atmosphere apparently underwent a complete change. Before that, there seems to have been no oxygen, but a great amount of carbonic acid gas; after that, oxygen must have become abundant in our atmosphere. This can be ascribed to the action of plants which, perhaps, appeared for the first time in sufficient numbers on earth 1,100 million years ago and purified our atmosphere. The presence of free oxygen, which is so important for terrestrial life, is now entirely due to plant photosynthesis.

Before plants and life started, the atmosphere of the earth probably resembled the present atmosphere of Venus, where carbonic acid gas is abundant, oxygen absent, and where no life on the present terrestrial pattern could reasonably exist. As the total age of the earth's crust is about 3,500 million years, two-thirds of this period witnessed a practically barren surface of our globe, and only during the last third of this time did life in some form become abundant. During the first, almost lifeless, 2,000-odd million years, the climatic conditions did not differ so very much from the present conditions as to make life impossible, as can be inferred from the chemical and physical properties of the sediments, and from scanty remains of marine plants. For some reason, life simply did not expand.

Nevertheless, remains of primitive plants, seaweeds or algae, are found in the ancient graphitic limestone near Bulawayo, South Rhodesia. Their age is about 2,700 million years, which sets back the origins of life quite near to the origin of the earth itself. As this discovery has been made but recently, we may think that the oldest vestiges of life have not yet been found, and that life started probably soon after the formation of the earth's crust. "Soon" may mean millions, or hundreds of millions of years; it is a short interval as compared with the age of the earth itself, although very long, not only by human standards, but also from the standpoint of geological, geochemical, and biological processes. During these first millions of years—and, probably, since then continuously until recent times—some germs of living matter could have been formed by the interaction of nonliving substances, the carbon-nitrogen-oxygen-hydrogen compounds. This could have taken place in stagnant pools of warm shallow shore water, on the cool bottom of the sea, or wherever the chemical and physical conditions of the environment were favorable; in any case, it must have happened in water.

Of course the synthesis of life, even its most primitive forms, has not yet succeeded in the laboratory. It may not succeed for a very long while. Actually, not much effort has been made until now in this direction to compete with the great diversity of conditions and the millions of years which Nature has had at her disposal. This, however, should not deter us from accepting the hypothesis of the start of life as here set forth.

The germs of life, once they came into being, started an evolutionary course towards higher and more diversified forms. The study of evolution covering the last 500

million years of the earth's history, for which abundant
data are available, shows that new forms—new species or
genera of animals and plants—are produced at the rate
of one new species within a few (2–10) million years
from each existing one. This leads to a doubling of the
number of species each 5 million years. After 100 million
years, one original species would have multiplied a mil-
lionfold (i.e., would have led to the origin of a million
new species; the number of individual organisms is not
considered here and is irrelevant). Of course, some of the
species would disappear, dying out. Nevertheless, once a
start was made, 100 million years would seem ample time
for the production of a highly diversified flora and fauna.

Yet, within some 2,000 million years, or twenty times
the above-mentioned space of time, nothing of the kind did
happen. Some remains of algae in South Africa, 2,700
million years old, as well as carbon of organic origin from
Lake Superior and Manitoba in Canada, 2,000 to 2,500
million years old, seem to indicate a scanty flora of seaweeds. About 1,200 to 1,400 million years ago a strange
marine organism called *Corycium enigmaticum* left its
traces in the rocks of Finland; one cannot tell whether it
was an animal or a plant. The plants during this early period seem to have been not only poor in species, but also
small in numbers, not being able to maintain an apprecia-
ble level of oxygen content in the atmosphere. Animals
may have been altogether absent.

The obstacle to the full development of life at this time
may have been of a climatic nature. As already mentioned, the average climate of the earth did not much differ from the present one. However, for good theoretical
reasons, the sun must have been slightly less luminous
(see Changes in the Sun, on p. 38), and the earth a few
degrees cooler, than at present. Periodical ice ages,
probably caused by dimming of solar radiation, have occurred on earth in the past with intervals of about 250
million years. When the sun itself was normally dimmer
than now, the abnormal lows of solar radiation during
ice ages may have caused the whole earth to freeze, from
pole to equator and from the surface almost to the bottom of the sea. The present writer has calculated that a
dimming of solar radiation by only 13 per cent, as compared with its present value, would lead to a globally com-

plete glaciation. This may have happened repeatedly during the early period of the earth's history, glaciation interrupting the progress of life before it could gain a full start. This may, perhaps, explain the poor development of life during the early 2,000 to 3,000 million years of the history of our globe. The cause of the interruption of organic development could, of course, have been a different one from that suggested here.

Apparently, since the Cambrian, no global interruption in the course of life has taken place. There were three major ice ages, 480, 240, and one million years ago (the last of which still persists, as is testified to by the glaciers of Greenland and the Antarctic); but none of them was of global extent, the tropical and even the temperate belts of the earth remaining free from ice and offering unrestricted breeding grounds to living organisms. This could explain why life has been almost explosive in its development during the recent period of the earth's history since the Paleozoic era, which began about 500 million years ago with a world-wide spread of trilobites, a now extinct class of marine animals, the nearest to which among living creatures would be, perhaps, wood lice and crabs.

4. The Rotation of the Earth

ASTROLOGERS LOOKED TO CELESTIAL PHENOMENA IN search of influences on the fate of human beings; they invented a complicated system according to which the courses of individual lives were determined by the configuration of the planets. Enlightened minds, including many astrologers themselves (e.g., Kepler), realized that astrology was nothing but superstition, yet the pressure of public opinion forced them to produce their "horoscopes."

Nevertheless, no one would doubt that celestial phenomena have an enormous influence on terrestrial life; although not on individuals, the influence is much greater and more general than that assumed by the astrologers. Life on our planet depends entirely upon the radiation of a star—our sun—and the motion of our planet determines how the beneficial radiation is distributed over its different parts.

Of all the celestial motions, the rotation of the earth

around its axis is the most important in this respect. The daily succession of light and darkness is its most obvious result. Equally important to us is the more uniform distribution and moderation of solar heat achieved by rotation. Were the rotation to slow down to, say, three hundred sixty-five days, the sun would stay more or less fixed with respect to the horizon: the hemisphere turned towards the sun would never enjoy the coolness and peace of night, but, although cloudy and constantly raining, would suffer from an infernal damp heat of some ninety degrees Fahrenheit (90°F); the other, dark hemisphere, plunged in eternal night and permanently frozen under a mostly clear sky, snowbound and ice-covered, would be just as unattractive.

The inclination of the axis of rotation to the ecliptic, or the orbital plane of the earth, is the well-known cause of the seasons. The alternation of summer and winter is its direct result, the Northern Hemisphere being turned towards the sun in June, away from it in December. The inclination of the axis also causes more solar heat to fall during the year in temperate and polar regions of the earth, making them warmer and diminishing the difference between the climatic zones. It is said that, were the axis at right angles to the ecliptic, permanent spring would reign all over the earth. However, in our latitudes this "spring" would amount to a permanent winter and glaciation, with an ice sheet about a mile thick covering Ireland, Scotland, England, Scandinavia, Canada, and the northeastern United States. The present inclination of the axis, 66.5°, is sufficient to make life possible in our latitudes. A still greater obliquity, corresponding, say, to 50° inclination, would render the climatic zones more uniform with respect to the mean annual temperature, with the climate of Italy reigning at the poles and all ice sheets melting away; the difference between the seasons —a hot summer and a cold winter—would, of course, become more pronounced.

A comparison of the observations of ancient eclipses with modern calculations indicates that the rate of rotation of the earth is gradually slowing down; the terrestrial "clock" has lost about 2 hours in 2,000 years. The duration of the day has increased by 1/50 of a second during this period. Tides have been suggested as a cause.

The tidal wave in the seas, traveling in a direction opposite to that of the rotation, produces friction and leads to a retardation. At the same time the moon experiences a counteraction from the tidal wave and is gradually driven away from the earth. Thus, the distance of the moon must have been less the farther we go back in time. It has been suggested that at a very remote epoch, perhaps 4,000 million years ago, the earth and the moon may have been one body, rotating very fast, the period of rotation only a few hours; and that the moon broke away from the earth and has been receding ever since, while the speed of rotation of the earth has been decreasing until it attained its present value. Modern researches indicate that the mechanism of interaction was more complicated.

First of all, it appears that the moon never formed part of the earth, but came into being somewhere outside our globe as an independent body; and second, all former theories of tidal evolution and changes in the rotation of the earth took into account only the oceanic tides. Recently it has been pointed out by Holmberg that tides of another kind, formerly disregarded, namely those in our atmosphere, play an important role, thus upsetting some of the old conclusions. The atmospheric tides, revealed by the diurnal variation of barometric pressure, are in tune or in "resonance" with the present period of rotation of the earth. Through a specific mechanism, sponsored by solar heat, these tides are working like a motor, tending to accelerate the earth's rotation; at present they compensate for some 30 per cent of tidal friction, but with a small increase in the length of the day their efficiency may increase many times, so that they automatically may keep the rate of rotation close to 24 hours, counteracting tidal friction in the seas. This state of affairs may have lasted for hundreds of millions of years or more, during which time the period of rotation of the earth did not change much. Therefore, in the beginning, the rotation of the earth must have been slower than was formerly supposed, perhaps some 12 hours instead of 4 to 5 hours, or shorter, as was believed until now; the possibility of the moon's having broken off from the earth because of fast rotation appears therefore to be still more unlikely. The recession of the moon, however, is not affected appreciably by the atmospheric tides, and is almost completely determined by tidal friction in terrestrial seas. The moon is constantly going away from the earth, irrespective of the changes in the rotation of the latter. The rate of rotation of the earth is likely to have been essentially constant over a long period of time.

What, then, about the observed retardation of rotation indicated by ancient eclipses? This is undoubtedly real, but must be considered as a transient phenomenon caused by climatic changes and the redistribution of water and ice masses over the earth's surface.

The main cause may be the following. During the Tertiary and the preceding 200 million years of a warm period in the earth's history, conditions were stable. The period of rotation differed very little from its "equilibrium" value, and the atmospheric tides, almost completely balanced tidal friction in the seas. Then, about a million years ago, the ice age began and a colder climate spread over the face of our globe. This must have affected the period of resonance of the atmospheric tides, making it slightly longer. The atmospheric tides no longer balanced friction, and the rotation of the earth began slowing down, at a rate of about 1 second in 100,000 years as presently observed. During the past million years the day may have increased by some 10 seconds—an insignificant quantity; it would have taken 10 million years to make good the lag in resonance. However, the ice age is expected to end long before that time; the resonance period will then decrease to its former value, and the slowing down of the rotation of the earth will cease.

This is a qualitative picture, suggested by the close coincidence of the period of oscillation of the atmosphere with 12 hours, or one half the present period of rotation of the earth; an accidental coincidence of this sort would be very unlikely, although not impossible.

An accurate theoretical calculation of the period of oscillation of the atmosphere is not yet possible. However, if the period depends on the velocity of sound, the climatic change which took place with the advent of the ice age must have changed the period by some 5 to 7 minutes, a quantity which is too large for the acceptance of our qualitative picture. In such a case the equilibrium between atmospheric and oceanic tides may have taken place before the Carboniferous, 250 million years ago. The equilibrium was then upset during the Permo-Carboniferous ice age of long duration, during which the length of the day increased over the average equilibrium value and has been increasing ever since. The present coincidence of the periods is then accidental, due to the temporary coolness of our climate, and the length of the day will continue to increase when our present ice age ends.

5. The Moon's Frozen Face

OF ALL THE PLANETS, ONLY THE EARTH HAS THE PRIVIlege of commanding a satellite of such considerable size in comparison with the mother planet. The moon's diameter is 2,160 miles, or only about 3½ times less than the diameter of the earth. The next largest ratio of satellite to planet diameter is that of Triton to Neptune, equal to 1/10, or three times less than for moon to earth. No wonder the moon occupies such an important place in terrestrial life, having been an influence on our calendar since ancient times, the major cause of ocean tides, the favorite patron of lovers, and figuring in so many other situations, true or imaginary.

In future the moon may enter our lives in a still more tangible form, when rocket-propelled spaceships land explorers and technicians on its barren surface. The strangeness of conditions encountered there will exceed everything hitherto experienced on earth. There is no atmosphere on the moon, and water is completely absent. There was a belief that a very thin atmosphere, perhaps 1/20,000 that of the earth, might exist on the moon, but recent observations have disproved this. Radio observations indicate that the density of the lunar atmosphere is less than one million millionth of the terrestrial. The lunar surface is exposed to a practically complete vacuum, and those landing on the moon must protect themselves with pressurized suits and oxygen-breathing apparatus.

The absence of an atmosphere leads to temperature extremes not encountered on earth. Although moon and earth are at practically the same distance from the sun, the sunrays at lunar noon may heat up the surface to 250°F, whereas on earth the temperature of desert sand will not exceed 150°F. At night the temperature of the lunar surface may drop to 300°F below freezing point. The long duration of the lunar day, almost equal to our month, helps to accentuate these extremes of temperature. There is no refreshing breeze to alleviate the intense daytime radiation of the sun, nor does there exist the blanket of moisture and clouds which protects us at night from the cold of space. With all these extremes, the moon, by our standards, is an ever-frozen world. The extreme heat and cold occur only on the very surface, whereas a few feet underneath an even cold persists, about 90°F below freezing point at the lunar equator and much lower at the poles. As compared with lunar conditions, even the ice-covered interior of Greenland might look like a Garden of Eden.

The surface of the moon is covered with a layer of dust at least 2 inches thick. The existence of this layer is proved beyond doubt by measurements of heat radiation from the moon's surface during lunar eclipses. When the earth's shadow cuts off sunlight from the moon, its surface cools off extremely fast; this indicates that little heat is supplied by the deeper layers of the soil, and that the surface material is an almost perfect insulator of heat; this could only be a fine powder of rock *in vacuo*, i.e., in empty space. No gas is contained between the grains of lunar dust, which makes it a very bad conductor of heat, unlike terrestrial dust where air helps the flow of heat between the dust grains.

The dust forms a protective layer which does not let solar heat penetrate into the soil, keeping it cold inside. During the lunar day, which lasts a fortnight, the surface becomes hot and radiates most of the received solar heat directly back to space, with very little flowing inwards. This explains why, even on the lunar equator where the sun provides on the average 50 per cent more heat than on the terrestrial equator (because there are no clouds on the moon), the temperature just underneath the surface remains lower than the coldest winter temperature of eastern Siberia or the Antarctic.

The lunar dust is probably caused by meteor impact. It would be wrong to imagine that meteor dust itself has deposited directly on the lunar surface. A fast particle of meteor dust hitting lunar rock would be instantly vaporized, and the vapors ejected back to space. But, at the point of impact an explosion would take place, shattering and pulverizing hundreds of times more material than the mass of the meteor that caused the explosion. The material resulting from the destruction of slow meteor dust grains may not leave the moon and may return to the lunar surface. In such a manner, during its thousands of millions of years of exposure to bombardment from space, the lunar surface has been battered into dust, composed partly of local, partly of meteoric, substance. On the mountain slopes the dust layer is thin and erosion intense; in the plains a thick layer—up to 40 inches—of dust may have collected, protecting the underlying surface from further erosion. This may explain the dissimilarity in appearance of various parts of the lunar surface, the different shades of brightness and coloration depending upon the original rock from which the dust was formed.

The lunar surface bears also the traces of impact of bodies larger than mere dust particles. Most of these bodies hit the moon in the beginning, when the moon and the earth were formed. Large bodies produced craters —the famous lunar craters, similar to meteor craters on earth—and also, by partly melting the surface rocks, lava flows. The lava flows often obliterated older craters, as is the case with the lunar *maria*, or "seas," which appear to be immense plains of solidified lava (of course, battered to dust at the surface). The lunar craters and plains appear to be the marks left on the surface of our satellite by the last planetesimals from which the moon was built (as the earth was). On earth the traces of impact have been erased long ago by erosion—the combined action of water, ice and wind; on the moon, where water and air are absent, the old scars have been preserved unchanged.

Of course, some meteor craters of recent origin are known on earth, and undoubtedly some more recent craters must exist on the moon, especially among those of smaller size. However, most of the big lunar craters must belong to the initial period of formation of our planetary system, testifying to times when our world was young.

The impact theory of formation of lunar craters, with

lava flows as a secondary phenomenon, is so well founded that it is generally accepted by leading scientists. Certain amateur circles still resist this explanation, disregarding, among other things, the evidence presented by meteor craters on earth; however, their opinion is hardly of any weight.

This reminds us of former attempts at explaining the origin of the moon and its surface features, against both the laws of physics and observational facts; such is Hörbiger's notorious Cosmic-ice Theory, which was at one time quite popular in lay and amateur circles. Hörbiger maintained that the moon consists of ice (as does, he thought, almost everything else in the universe). Were this so, water vapor from the ice would have provided the moon with an atmosphere and clouds; these, however, are known to be completely absent. Thus, when we refer to the moon's "frozen face," we wish only to imply that it is very cold there; actually, there is no substance to freeze, no water, either in gaseous, liquid, or solid form—no ice, only dry dust at the surface and solid rock underneath.

The absence of air and water on the moon is explained by its small gravitational pull; all these substances would evaporate "quickly," i.e., within a few hundred thousand years, and disappear into surrounding interplanetary space. If the moon ever possessed a supply of air and water, it must have lost it within a relatively short interval of time as compared with its age. Similarly, all gases from volcanic sources will be lost from the moon currently as they reach the surface.

The absence of an atmosphere means that life is not possible on the moon; it is doomed to be a dead world not merely by a fortuitous absence of the materials so needed for life, but by its small size and gravitation, which render it unable to keep these materials firmly bound at the surface (as does the earth).

6. The Origin of the Moon

AS ALREADY MENTIONED, BY RELATIVE SIZE THE MOON IS the largest satellite of the solar system. As to absolute dimensions, only five satellites exceed or equal it in mass:

three of Jupiter, one of Saturn, and one of Neptune. The largest by mass are Neptune's Triton, Jupiter's Ganymede, and Saturn's Titan, each equal to about twice the moon. Thus, although not the largest absolutely, the moon comes pretty close. With a diameter of 2,160 miles, it is more than a satellite—it is another planet. The system earth-moon is a double planet, unique in the solar neighborhood; as seen from Mars or Venus, this system would look like a second wonder of the solar family, after the rings of Saturn: a brilliant blue planet, the earth, with a first-magnitude yellowish starlet, the moon, circling the principal body at an apparent distance of about ½ a degree, or about that of the lunar diameter as seen by the terrestrial observer.

This remarkable system must have come into being in an equally remarkable manner. The tides offer at least a partial clue to the problem. Tides are caused by unequal attraction of the moon and the sun upon different parts of the earth's surface. The tidal wave of the terrestrial seas travels around the earth and by friction opposes its rotation, which is slowed down. Each action has its counteraction, and so the bulge of the tidal wave pulls the moon and forces it to recede from the earth. Therefore, in the past the moon must have been nearer to us and the earth rotating faster. Such considerations led Sir George Darwin, son of the famous naturalist, to visualize a time in the distant past when earth and moon were close together, rotating as one body around a common axis, the time of rotation a few hours only. Some kind of "resonance vibration" caused the breakup of the body, already greatly distorted by centrifugal force. This was the birth of the moon which separated from the mother body on account of centrifugal force, and was then driven farther and farther away by tidal action. Darwin calculated that the time of origin must have been only 150 million years ago. However, his figure is too small; Jeffreys showed that the tides work much more slowly than Darwin supposed, and that the whole process must have taken several thousand million years. An exact figure cannot be set, because tidal friction depends to a great degree on the distribution and bottom structure of the seas, which have varied greatly over the ages. Further, it became probable that the moon could not have separated from the earth itself, but must have come into being at a certain distance from it. The time when this happened and the moon began receding from its original position probably coincided with the beginning of the solar system, about 3,500 to 4,500 million years ago.

Nevertheless, the possibility of the moon's having broken off from the earth cannot be entirely ruled out. Certainly this could not have happened while life existed here; the tidal force alone of the departing moon would have extinguished all traces of it. The tidal force must then have been 200,000 times greater than now, and not only the oceans, but the whole earth's crust would have followed the revolving young moon in an infernal turmoil of fragments of rock and molten lava, forming a wave at least 100 miles high. If this did happen, the moon itself must have broken up into smaller fragments, which collected into the present body on reaching a safe distance from the disturbing earth. It is possible that the separation took place, not from the present solid earth, but from a body of larger size and lower density, which only later became the present earth and moon.

The Pacific Ocean is sometimes regarded as the scar left on the earth's surface by the newborn moon. An objection raised against this hypothesis on the ground that the Pacific Ocean is too shallow a depression to have contained the moon is somewhat naive and, of course, invalid: the deep hole left behind by the moon would have been filled with plastic material from the depths, which, under pressures of several hundred thousand atmospheres, would flow like a liquid even if it were solid rock by ordinary standards. A shallow depression is just what could be expected after the separation. If, nevertheless, many scientists reject this hypothesis, it is because calculations of tidal evolution indicate that the moon could never have been nearer than 9,000 miles from the earth's center, or 5,000 miles from its surface. Therefore, if the original earth was as big as that (which is improbable), the scar left by the moon would have disappeared afterwards, when the earth contracted. On the other hand, if the earth was never much bigger than now, the moon could not have touched the earth; it must either have originated at this minimum distance of 9,000 miles or arrived from a greater distance as an independent body which came into being in the solar system without any intervention by its foster parent, the earth. This conclusion is irrefutable if, from the beginning, the sun, earth, and moon had the same masses as now, and if there have been no other important bodies in our vicinity which could have altered the course of events, and disappeared later on.

Now, these *ifs* are by no means certain. On the contrary, in the beginning the mass of the earth may have been considerably greater than now, at the expense of light gases which since then have evaporated into space; and there must then have been many stray bodies in the solar system which, before they were eliminated by collision, could have come near the earth-moon system and influenced it by gravitation or contact.

Therefore, despite the clear outcome of the mathematical theory, it is still possible that the moon broke away from the earth some 4,000 million years ago. What happened during the time between the breakoff and the moment when the distance of 9,000 miles was reached, cannot be told from mathematics, because the conditions which prevailed during those fateful hours and days are not known. In any case, there was not yet a moon in the present sense—no compact body, but a swarm of millions of fragments into which the detached mass was crushed by the enormous tidal force of the earth.

The mathematical history of the moon begins only at the above-mentioned distance of 9,000 miles from the earth. It is possible that from the moment the moon reached this distance, or was born there, the unknown factors ceased to exist; in that case the mathematical picture of the ensuing evolution should be more or less correct. A remarkable coincidence speaks in favor of this belief. The distance of 9,000-odd miles, which is the minimum distance of the moon according to theory, is practically equal to the so-called Roche's limit, or the closest distance at which the moon could exist as an integral body; at closer distances it would have been broken up by tidal action of the earth. In other words, the mathematical history of the moon began exactly where it should have begun—at the distance where the cloud of ejected fragments was permitted to gather into one body.

It is very unlikely that the coincidence is fortuitous. It makes it quite probable that the moon was actually formed at that distance, either from ejected fragments, or from matter found there "on the spot."

Nevertheless, there is the other possibility that the moon met the earth as a stranger from outside, was captured by the earth's tidal action, approached down to a distance of 9,000 miles and then began receding, until the present distance of 240,000 miles was reached. This possibility, although less probable than that of a common origin, cannot be ruled out. It has the beauty of mathematical precision and simplicity. The time of capture of the moon may have been, in this case, at a later epoch, not necessarily coinciding with the origin of the solar system. Indeed, calculations yield a figure of about 2,500 million years ago for the time of capture of the moon, some 1,000 to 2,000 million years after the beginning. At this time interplanetary space must have been well cleaned up and free from stray bodies, and the assumption in the mathematical theory about the absence of other considerable bodies in our vicinity is no longer contradictory. All fits well into the scheme; so that if beauty and simplicity were the substitute for the unknown true state of affairs, the theory of external capture of the moon should be preferred. However, nature does not necessarily solve its problems in the simplest manner.

It may be added that the effect of atmospheric tides, mentioned earlier (see The Rotation of the Earth, p. 21) and not yet taken into account in the mathematical theory of tidal evolution of the earth-moon system, would turn the odds considerably in favor of the theory of capture from outside. With the atmospheric tides resisting the retardation of the earth's axial rotation, the speed of rotation could not have varied in the course of time to the extent required by the unamended tidal theory. In the beginning, the rotation must have been rather slow—too slow for rotational breakup and separation of the moon from the earth.

It must also be pointed out that, if the capture theory is correct, before capture the moon could not have been somewhere in distant regions of space, but must have circled the sun in an orbit which did not much differ from that of the earth, approaching the latter from time to time until tidal capture took place at a close approach. Having been formed in the same regions of the solar system, from the same wisp of the original nebula, the earth and the moon could still be considered to some extent of common origin, more closely related to each other than the more distant planets are.

It cannot yet be decided which of the theories of the origin of the moon is to be finally accepted—the tidal breakoff from the earth, the independent formation at a distance of 9,000 miles or more, or the capture theory. In any case, the later fate of our satellite, after it came —in whatever manner—to this minimum distance, leaves no room for doubt: it was receding from the earth, is still doing so, and will continue for a long time in the future.

7. Solar Eclipses

IN OLD DAYS THE DISAPPEARANCE OF THE SUN DURING an eclipse caused fear and consternation, because people did not know the cause of this phenomenon and were afraid of losing the sun forever. Now most people know the explanation and an eclipse evokes more curiosity than fear.

Solar eclipses are caused by the moon's placing itself between sun and earth and casting its shadow on the latter. An observer from the earth sees the sun partially or completely obscured by the dark circle of the moon as it moves across the solar disk. Solar eclipses can happen, of course, only at new moon and only when the apparent path of the moon passes over the sun's disk at that time. An eclipse may be partial or total, according to whether a part or the whole of the solar disk is covered; in an annular eclipse a narrow rim of the sun remains visible around the dark body of the moon. The shadow of the moon may fall on different parts of our globe, and an eclipse observable in one part of the earth as total may be visible as partial, or not visible at all, in another.

The total eclipse of the sun on June 30, 1954, was undoubtedly one of the most outstanding astronomical events of recent years. The total phase was visible along a narrow strip on the earth's surface about 93 miles wide, over which the full shadow of the moon was passing, traveling from west to east at a speed of about 1,700 miles an hour.

The path of the totality passed over the North Atlantic through Thorshavn in the Faroes toward Bergen in Norway, southern Sweden and the Swedish island of Öland in the Baltic. The duration of totality in the middle of the strip was 2½ minutes. In Ireland and Great Britain the eclipse was visible only as partial, the major part but not all of the sun's disk being covered by the moon; at the greatest phase 70 to 90 per cent of the sun's diameter was covered; the unobscured part appeared then as a narrow crescent lying on its back, the horns stretching upwards.

Special astronomical expeditions are sent into the paths of total solar eclipses to study various phenomena which cannot be observed in daylight. The outer portion of the solar atmosphere, called the chromosphere, which flashes as a narrow bright arc just before and just after totality, is observed spectroscopically. The silvery nebulous aureole, or corona, apparently representing an extension of the solar atmosphere into interplanetary space, is perhaps the chief object of study.

The solar corona is composed partly of gas and, at greater distances from the sun, partly of meteoric dust; its fainter parts seem to reach beyond the orbit of the earth. The earth is actually moving inside the outskirts of the corona, which are known as the *zodiacal light;* the importance of these studies is, therefore, obvious.

There are many other observations which can be made during an eclipse. However, on such an occasion, time is rather short; during the precious minutes of totality, when the glare of the solar limb is obscured, the observers have to fulfill a prescribed program, consisting mostly in photographic observations and limited to one or two items only. Many interesting problems cannot be tackled for lack of time.

In former days searches were made during eclipses for planets which might be revolving close to the sun and could not be seen normally in full daylight. More than once, the discovery of a planet inside the orbit of Mercury was announced. The new planet was even given a name, that of Vulcan. However, these discoveries were not verified later and must have been due to some mistakes made by the observers. During the few minutes of totality the haste and excitement of the observers may have caused them to identify some fixed star, or perhaps a comet, with the desired planet. Thus, the searches for intra-Mercurial planets have ended in complete disappointment. It is now more or less certain that Vulcan does not exist, at least not as a body of considerable size.

The mere fact that a total eclipse was observed at a certain time and locality is of great importance when it refers to past ages. Historical records of ancient eclipses in the region of the Mediterranean have shown that 2,000 years ago the eclipses occurred about 1,600 miles to the east of the localities "predicted" from modern data. This is explained by changes in the speed of rotation of the earth, which rotated slightly faster in the past than at present. The main cause of the changes was thought to be tidal friction in the oceans; it seems, however, that matters are more complicated (see Chapters 4 and 6). In addition to the long-range competition between oceanic and atmospheric tides, the speed of rotation of the earth may change over shorter periods on account of the transport of water masses from the poles to the equator or in the opposite direction, caused by melting or accumulation of polar ice. The changes revealed by solar eclipses may have been considerably influenced by these events. The inertia of the slowly rotating polar melt-water when transported to the equator resists the faster rotation at the equator and makes the rotation of the whole earth slower; and vice versa. When the Great Ice melted 10,000 years ago, the length of the day may have increased by as much as 1 second. After the warm postglacial period of about 5,000 to 7,000 years ago the climate of the earth became somewhat colder, and some ice accumulated in Greenland and the Antarctic; as a consequence, the rotation of the earth became slightly faster. In more recent times, during the past 2,000 years, some melting of ice seems to have taken place again, causing the period of rotation to increase. These changes are reflected in the records of ancient eclipses, as well as in modern observations.

Thus the study of solar eclipses reveals new information about the rotation of the earth, the tides, and even about climatic changes. It is a typical example of how different branches of science depend upon one another.

8. Solar Heat

WHEN AUTUMN IS PAVING THE WAY FOR WINTER'S ADvent, when the leaves wither and fall and days shorten, the cold reminds us of the cause of these changes—the star nearest to us, our sun. It not only governs, by its gravitation, the paths of the earth and its sister bodies called planets which circle around their master, each in its proper orbit, but by its radiation influences also the happenings on the surface of the planets, on earth in particular, where nature responds to all the changes which solar radiation undergoes.

Solar radiation, combined with the inclination of the earth's axis, is the well-known cause of the seasons. In winter the solar rays strike the surface of the earth obliquely, and the days are short. In our latitudes, therefore, only a small amount of solar heat is transmitted to the surface, an amount insufficient to cope with the radiation losses to space, and the temperature drops. By withdrawing its heat, the sun reminds us of its existence, which we are but too likely to forget during happy summer days or in milder climates.

The reminder, however, is a gentle one, especially on the east side of the Atlantic, where even in winter the average temperature keeps around the forties, well above freezing point. Were we to feel the full effect of the withdrawal of solar heat, i.e., were there no supply of heat from other, warmer places of the earth, the temperature in the British Isles would drop to $-100°F$ in November (or January), and to $-135°F$ in December. These figures are based on well-known physical laws of radiation. Fortunately, however, with respect to the weather we are not isolated from the rest of the world. The messenger of the sun, the wind, set in motion by unequal heating of the surface of the earth, sees to it that solar heat stored in ocean waters during the summer, or in warmer climates, is transported to those places most in need of it.

A system of "central heating," represented by the atmospheric and oceanic currents, is thus at work, maintained by solar radiation itself. Because of the equalization of extremes by these currents, the temperature on the earth's surface nowhere drops to the above-mentioned catastrophic limits, not even in the continental areas of Siberia or Canada, which are the farthest to reach by the soft oceanic winds, nor at the Poles, where in winter solar radiation is absent. In other words, owing to atmospheric circulation, even in midwinter Ireland and Britain are allowed to spend 90 per cent of their summer share of solar heat, although the direct solar radiation amounts to only 10 to 20 per cent. To improve the situation we have coal, whose heat is again solar energy, stored by growing plants 200 million years ago. Thus, the sun is looking after us in winter as well as in summer. In spite of their cloudy sky, the British Isles are better provided in winter with solar heat than many other, sunnier places in the world.

Where does the solar heat come from? The sun is 330,-000 times heavier than the earth, and weighs 2,000 million million million million tons. If this mass were all ordinary fuel, it would last for a couple of thousand years only—so enormous is the energy expended by the sun. The history of mankind is much longer than 2,000 years, and geology, the history of the earth, tells us that the sun has been shining for time intervals a million times longer than that. Until a century ago the source of solar energy was a complete puzzle, and only now have we got to the root of this riddle. The only kind of fuel which is adequate for maintaining solar radiation is atomic fuel. And, indeed, theoretical considerations strengthened by physical experiment and astronomical observations indicate that in the interior of the sun conditions are favorable for the development of atomic energy.

The central temperature of the sun is between 20 and 30 million degrees centigrade, which is about the temperature obtained at the explosion of an atom bomb. At this temperature atomic fuel is slowly burning, at a rate sufficient to provide the energy radiated by the sun, and sufficient to maintain the radiation for time intervals in future several times longer than those past.

The fuel is ordinary hydrogen, not its explosive isotope

tritium used in the hydrogen bomb. Four hydrogen atoms combine gradually into one helium atom, a process which can proceed slowly and directly at "lower" temperatures of about 15 million degrees, but can be greatly accelerated by the presence of carbon at higher temperatures; the carbon itself is not used up, but merely plays the role of a *catalyst*—an intermediary agent in the process, the so-called "carbon cycle" in the energy production of the sun. The store of hydrogen in the sun is sufficient to maintain its radiation for thousands of millions of years; indeed, since the origin of the solar system the sun has burned an amount of hydrogen equal to only 4 per cent of its mass.

9. Changes in the Sun and the Destiny of Life

EARTHLY LIFE DEPENDS ENTIRELY ON SOLAR RADIATION, which not only maintains a comfortable range of temperature over the surface of our planet, but provides the chemical energy for plant growth and the building up of foodstuffs, like starches and sugars, as well as for the production of the oxygen of our atmosphere. Even the air we breathe is a product of sunlight, without which we would suffocate!

In the preceding chapter we learned that unequal distribution of solar heat over the earth's surface is remedied by air and ocean currents. These, however, would not help were the solar radiation itself to change. If the solar output of heat dropped by only 15 per cent below its present level, an ice age covering the whole earth from pole to equator, with glaciers a mile thick, would exterminate all higher life on the earth's surface. Were the radiation to rise by 60 per cent, equally fatal consequences to life would result from excessive heat.

A study of the climatic conditions on earth in the past makes it seem highly probable that the radiation of the sun has been changing. The very warm climate of the Tertiary, 50 million years ago, would suggest that solar radiation was then higher than now by about 9 per cent. During the ice ages, or, rather, during their coldest periods, the sun may have radiated 7 to 10 per cent less heat than now. Actually, we are at present still in an ice age, although not in its coldest phase. The cold periods have never lasted very long, as compared with the warm periods which appear to correspond to the normal level of solar radiation.

Thus, as with all material things, the sun may change and the conditions of life on earth may be affected. The theoretical study of the internal structure of the sun has brought us nearer to the understanding of these changes.

Modern knowledge of physical laws has led to the calculation of the conditions inside the sun, and to a prediction of how it changes in the course of time. To someone not acquainted with the present state of physical and mathematical knowledge it might seem hopeless to try to describe the behavior of matter at temperatures of tens of millions of degrees and at enormous pressures which cannot be produced in the laboratory. However, the experimental position is not as hopeless as it seems. The mutual interaction of the atoms of a gas depends upon the velocity of their relative motion, which is a measure of the temperature. Heat means random motion, in all directions. In the laboratory, nonrandom velocities of atoms in one direction are obtained which are equivalent to temperatures up to thousands of millions of degrees, a thousand times higher than in stellar interiors; the properties of atoms at collisions of this speed are well investigated, and predictions can be made for cases which cannot be precisely imitated in the laboratory. The success of the atom bomb is an indication that in this respect scientists are on the right track.

Therefore, the behavior of gaseous matter at temperatures and pressures which prevail in stellar interiors is quite well known; actually, it is better known than, for example, the properties of solids at ordinary temperatures. It is thus possible to describe the internal structure and development of the sun and other stars if their chemical composition is given. Because the composition is not known exactly, the conclusions are only approximate.

The sun's fuel is atomic: it is hydrogen, which is being gradually converted into helium. The fuel is nonexplosive; we need not fear it, although its name reminds us of the hydrogen bomb. Hydrogen is "burning" only in the central, hottest parts of the sun; there is little mixing, and in the outside, comprising 75 per cent of the solar mass, the fuel remains unused. As hydrogen is being continually replaced by helium in the innermost regions, the chemical composition of the deep interior differs more and more from that of the outer regions; a peculiar "composite" structure for the sun results, with a core in which the proportion of hydrogen decreases with time. Calculations indicate that, as a consequence of these internal changes, the radiation of the sun must gradually increase. The increase is very slow, noticeable only over hundreds of millions of years, but it is accelerated as time goes on.

The increase of solar radiation as the sun's fuel is used up might seem to be a paradox; yet a fireplace works in the same way (although for other reasons), being hottest when a considerable portion of the fuel has burned away.

The gradual warming up of the sun seems to be interrupted by periodic dimming, a consequence of certain upheavals or mixing in the deep interior which can be foreseen theoretically. The dimming causes ice ages on earth, recurring after intervals of 240 million years. During the last 500 million years there are known to have been three major ice ages: the Eocambrian, 480 million years ago; the Permo-Carboniferous, 230 million years ago; and the Quaternary ice age which started a few million years ago. Each major ice age lasted only a few million years, and showed great fluctuations of climate—intense glacial periods, or "minor ice ages," of great cold alternating with warmer interglacial periods within time intervals of the order of 100,000 years. At present we are amid the Quaternary ice age, although not at its peak: our time falls into a warm interglacial period which began about 10,000 years ago. The average temperature of the earth is now 58°F, whereas during the colder periods of recent glaciation, a few hundred thousand years ago, it may have been as low as 40°F. In the Tertiary and earlier, before the ice age began, it was much warmer for a long period of about 200 million years of "normal" existence, and when the present ice age ends, after hundreds of thousands, or millions, of years, the mean temperature of our globe will rise again to the Tertiary level of 72°F, with a climate of Florida in Britain and Ireland and with forests of beech and oak in place of the present glaciers of Greenland and the Antarctic. We do not know when this time will come; if we could judge by analogy with the Permo-Carboniferous ice age, which lasted for about 25 million years, we could not expect the present one to end earlier than, say, 15 to 20 million years hence, because it began only a few million years ago. In any case, present humanity will hardly see the end of it.

Although lasting for millions of years, the ice age is but a transient episode in the life history of the sun and earth. It will end when the sun regains its normal brightness; the sun will thereafter shine for hundreds of millions of years with an intensity sufficient to melt the polar ices on earth and to maintain all over the surface of our globe a climate like that of the Garden of Eden. Will there be man in the future Eden, or his more advanced successor? Or will mankind be extinct, and only animals roam this coming wild paradise?

The gradual increase of solar radiation will continue, and the climate of the earth will become warmer. Beginning with 72°F after the end of the present ice age, the mean temperature will rise to 79°F after 660 million years, to 86°F after 920 million years. At that time it will become rather hot in equatorial regions, where the mean annual temperature may reach 98°F; life will have to take refuge in the polar regions of the earth. Yet the changes in the internal structure of the sun will continue relentlessly; they will become much more rapid than before and, as the hydrogen near the center of the sun is completely converted into helium, the sun will change from a "dwarf" star into a "subgiant" of greater size and luminosity. Within, say, 1,100 million years from now, the radiation of the sun will increase to three times its present value, heating up the earth to 257°F, well above the boiling point of water. As far as life on earth is concerned, this will be the end; everything will perish in this fatal heat wave.

Of course, if populated by intelligent beings of an advanced technique, the surface of the earth may come to be protected from the lethal radiation by the inventiveness of these beings (we would hesitate to call them human; the human race will hardly persist for 1,000 million years). For example, they might create a cloud in space around the earth, composed of fine dust or smoke, which would shield them from the excessive solar radiation, letting through only so much solar heat as is required for a comfortable existence. The task does not seem insurmountable even for present humanity, if its technical genius continues its advances at the same pace as in the past. The technical development of the human race has been going on for only 10,000 years, with most of the spectacular achievements dating from the last few centuries, yet man is already launching artificial satellites into space. The warning of the impending heat wave will come 100 million years beforehand, which is 10,000 times 10,-000 years. There would be plenty of time to get ready for the emergency, provided there were intelligent beings to take care of it. If not, the heat wave would mean the end of life on earth.

The timetable given above need not be considered exact. The heat wave may arrive a few hundred million years earlier or later. Qualitatively, however, the suggested course of events, caused by the internal changes and evolution of the sun, appears to be highly probable.

After the heat wave the sun and the planets will continue to exist. The sun may shine for several thousand million years more, until it either becomes a "white dwarf," a shrunken small body of low luminosity, or explodes as a supernova and disperses into space. Everything must have an end; the sun and the solar system cannot be exceptions to this general rule.

10. The Spectrum

THE SUN AND THE STARS—WHICH ARE OTHER, DISTANT suns similar to our own—emit white light. The true color of sunlight becomes evident when reflected from the surface of snow, clouds, or other substances that reflect equally all kinds of light that fall upon them. We call these substances white, but obviously it is the incident light that is white. Snow illuminated by red light will appear red, and so also may clouds appear at sunset when the color of the setting sun is changed by absorption in our atmosphere.

White is not a simple color. The sunbeam consists of

light of different colors. This is obvious from the coloration of various objects: green leaves reflect green, the petals of a rose red light, absorbing other colors. The reflected colored light comes from the sun. Thus, white sunlight contains all imaginable colors, white being simply their mixture.

In a rainbow, sunlight is decomposed into its colors; this is caused by light passing through raindrops in a very particular way. The colors in the rainbow are arranged in a definite order: red, yellow, green, blue, violet, with all the transitions in between. This is called the spectrum of sunlight. A spectrum may be produced by passing light through a crystal, a diamond, or a piece of suitably shaped glass. Physicists and astronomers use glass prisms for obtaining spectra.

Light has the properties of wave motion, similar to waves on a water surface. The distance between the crests of two waves is called the *wavelength*. Each spectrum color has its own wavelength; in fact, color and wavelength denote one and the same thing. The wavelength of red light is 1/36,000, of blue light 1/60,000 of an inch; for intermediate colors it is intermediate.

With the aid of prisms, the spectrum from a light source can be obtained, and the wavelength of any part of the spectrum accurately measured. Nowadays this is done most successfully by photography. The method itself is known as spectrum analysis.

The applications of spectrum analysis in astronomy are numberless; most of our knowledge of the physical properties and motions of the stars is due to this method.

Thus, the spectrum reveals the chemical composition of the gaseous envelopes, or atmospheres, of celestial bodies. Each gaseous substance contained in the atmosphere absorbs light of a few distinct colors or wavelengths, producing gaps or narrow dark lines in the spectrum. Various substances produce different lines, the positions of which—their wavelengths or accurate colors—can be determined in the laboratory. By comparing the laboratory data with the lines revealed by the spectrum of a celestial object, the substances contained in its atmosphere can be identified. It is thus found that the sun and the stars consist of all the elements known on earth, and more or less in the same proportion. The constituent bodies of our universe are built out of the same mixture of elements. This would suggest a common origin for all these bodies.

When a body moves towards the observer, the waves of its light will arrive more frequently, and their crests will be separated by smaller intervals: the wavelength of a spectral line decreases, and the color of the line changes slightly; the line will be displaced toward the blue-violet end of the spectrum. When the body moves away from the observer, the lines will be displaced towards the red. By measuring these minute changes of color, or *Doppler shifts,* the velocities of approach and recession of celestial bodies can be determined.

Thus, the spectrum provides us with a marvelous means of determining the motion of distant objects. We need not see the motion or wait for the displacement of the body; the change in color of the spectral lines tells us instantly whether the distance of the light source is increasing or decreasing, and also gives the speed of this motion, the so-called *radial velocity.* Of course, small velocities cannot be easily detected by this method, and for terrestrial motions the Doppler-shift method is of no practical value. Celestial bodies, however, move with velocities of many miles per second; such velocities are already measurable by the spectroscopic method, which is especially convenient because it is equally effective with nearby and distant objects, provided they are not too far away to become unobservable.

The rotation of planets and the sun, the motions of stars in the Milky Way system, the rotation of our Milky Way and of other galaxies (*extragalactic* or "spiral" *nebulae*) millions of light years away are revealed by the spectrum. The most spectacular achievement of the Doppler-shift method is the discovery of the recession of the extragalactic nebulae: the whole universe, to the very limits of observable space, appears to be expanding in all directions. This again suggests that there was a beginning, 4,000 to 5,000 million years ago, when the universe exploded from a very small volume, and that all presently existing celestial bodies are fragments created in this explosion and still flying apart.

Of the other data which spectrum analysis can yield, one could mention: the temperature and pressure on the surface of celestial bodies and the density of their atmospheres; in combination with photometric (intensity-of-light) data and accurate measurements of position—the radius, volume, luminosity and mass of distant stars; the luminosity and distance of extragalactic nebulae; the magnetic force on the surface of the sun and stars; the rotation of stars (which is a different problem from that of the rotation of nearby objects of visible dimensions; the stars are so far away that no disk is visible). Briefly, a ray of light from a celestial body contains an unbelievable wealth of information which the spectrum helps to decipher. Spectrum analysis has become the most powerful means of investigating the properties of celestial bodies, including the structure and origin of the universe itself.

11. The Solar Atmosphere

SOLAR HEAT ORIGINATES FROM NUCLEAR REACTIONS IN the deep interior of the sun. However, the heat of the interior does not reach us directly—a fortunate circumstance, because it would kill us. Shielded by the immense body of the sun, the heat seeps gradually outwards. The direct transmitter of solar radiation to space is the surface, which thus, of all the surfaces of celestial bodies, is of most concern to us, ranking in importance with the surface of our own abode of life.

The solar surface is not solid like that of the earth and some other planets; nor is it an ocean of liquid molten lava or metal, as was fancied sometimes in the good old days when scientists first began wondering about the structure of other heavenly bodies. The surface temperature of the sun is so high—5,700 degrees centigrade or over 10,000 degrees Fahrenheit—that all existing substances are vaporized and at the same time decomposed or *dissociated* into the simple bodies or elements of which they consist. Thus, water will not exist at the solar temperature, even in the form of vapor; instead, it will break up into hydrogen and oxygen, and the mixture of these gases, highly explosive on earth, will be unable to explode, the high temperature keeping the atoms of these constituents apart. Carbon, "coal," in the form of vapor, mixed with oxygen, will not burn. A chunk of iron, if thrown into the sun, would experience a fate similar to that of a drop of water on red-hot iron: it would boil up intensely and disappear in an instant, being converted into vapor that would mix with the rest of the atmosphere. Incidentally, such chunks are constantly falling into the sun; they are called *meteorites* and can be observed when they enter our atmosphere.

Thus, the solar surface is all gas: nay, the whole sun is nothing but a continuous atmosphere, if this word is applied in the same sense as on earth. Nevertheless, astronomers have agreed to call "atmosphere" only the outer layers of the gaseous solar envelope, those layers which are visible and accessible to direct observation. As we proceed inwards, the solar gases become less transparent and there is a level through which we cannot see; this level, the *photosphere,* represents the visible surface of the sun. Everything above the photosphere is called *atmosphere,* although there is no sharp distinction between this and the underlying "surface"; all is gas, down to the very center of the sun.

Spectrum analysis shows that the solar gases represent a mixture of probably all the 92 existing permanent elements, from hydrogen to uranium; a few elements which are not certainly identified may be there, but either their amounts are too small or their spectral lines are too difficult to observe. The mixture is more or less uniform, atoms of each element being everywhere present in the same relative proportion. However, the light gases hydrogen and helium are by far the most abundant, all the other elements together amounting to less than 1 per cent, probably to about 0.1 per cent, by weight. In this respect the chemical composition of the solar atmosphere differs very much from that of the earth, where hydrogen and helium are represented by about one part in ten thousand, the very opposite of what is found in the sun. Nevertheless, it is believed that both the earth and the sun originated from the same cosmic mixture of the elements, from a vast nebula and dust cloud that gave birth to the solar system some 4,500 million years ago. This is supported by the relative abundance of the heavier elements, which is essentially the same in the earth's crust, in the solar atmosphere, and in meteorites, which may be considered samples of material from other, broken-up, planets. Excluding hydrogen and helium, the most abundant elements in all heavenly bodies so far explored are oxygen, magnesium, silicon, and iron; the other, less common elements occur in more or less the same proportions in the sun and on earth.

How then is the enormous difference between the amounts of the light gases in the sun and the earth to be accounted for? The explanation is that, in the process of formation, the gravitational attraction of the earth was not strong enough to hold the light gases firmly; even now, hydrogen and helium will escape to interplanetary space from the earth's atmosphere, because the molecules of these substances may move with greater speed than the attraction of the earth can offset. These gases will simply "evaporate" into space. The solar attraction is much greater than that of the earth and will not let the light gases escape. Therefore, the solar atmosphere may truly represent the primordial mixture of the elements, whereas the earth as a whole (crust and core) has lost most of its hydrogen and helium. However, with respect to the other elements the earth, too, may be regarded as a fair sample of the original mixture.

Dark spots are sometimes visible on the surface of the sun. To observe them, a small telescope suffices. However, do not look at the sun directly through a telescope; either use a dark glass in front of the eyepiece, or project the image of the sun on a sheet of white paper placed behind the eyepiece.

Two hundred years ago sunspots were thought to be dark, solid islands floating in an ocean of molten lava. Modern investigations have proved beyond doubt that the spots are as gaseous as the rest of the sun; they are not even as dark as they appear against the more luminous background of the rest of the solar surface. The temperature in sunspots is about 4,000°C, as compared with 5,700° for the average surface. Thus, sunspots are hotter than the hottest ovens on earth, their temperature being about that of the crater of an electric arc, and their light emission per square inch about as intense as in the arc; they appear dark only because the surrounding surface is brighter still. Spectroscopic studies have shown that in the spots the gases rise from the interior of the sun and flow out in all directions. Sunspots are vortices of gas, like cyclones, thunderstorms, or tornadoes in the terrestrial atmosphere. The rising gases cool off because of the release of pressure and expansion, which makes their temperature lower than that of the nonrising surroundings. The cause of the relatively low temperature of sunspots is the same as that of the cold on mountaintops or in high altitudes on earth.

Sunspots are not always equally visible on the sun. There are years when sunspots are absent, and other years when they are abundant. The number of sunspots varies, with an average period of 11 years, which is called the *sunspot cycle*. The spacing between sunspot maxima, or those years when sunspots are most numerous, is not always 11 years; it fluctuates, mostly between 10 and 12 years, but greater deviations (from 7 to 16 years) have occurred. Recent sunspot maxima occurred in 1905, 1917, 1928, 1937, 1947 and 1957. Various phenomena, not only on the sun but also on earth, follow the rhythm of the sunspot cycle. Thus, aurorae (the northern and southern lights) are directly connected with sunspots, and are most frequent in the years of sunspot maxima. Aurorae are caused by *corpuscular emission* or electrically charged hydrogen atoms (protons), ejected from the solar surface with velocities of over 1,000 miles per second; they produce luminescence when they hit the upper atmospheric strata on earth. Sunspots and their surroundings are the chief sources of corpuscular emission, which explains the correlation with aurorae.

The corpuscular radiation causes "magnetic storms" on earth, during which the compass goes wrong. The electrical currents which produce the storms seem to have a mysterious influence on terrestrial life. They influence plant growth, either directly or through rainfall, as is revealed by the annual rings of growth in ancient trees (especially in semiarid regions) which reflect the 11-year sunspot cycle. There is a curious coincidence which hardly can be attributed to chance: the years of European revolutions, 1789 (France), 1830 (France), 1848 (France and elsewhere), 1870 (France), 1905 (Russia), 1917 (Russia), 1937 (Spain), 1956 (Hungary) are all on, or within only a year of, sunspot maxima. It would suggest an indirect influence of the corpuscular radiation on mass psychology. Of course, revolutions are caused by economic and political factors, not by sunspots; but it may be that the spots trigger off the revolutions by literally "electrifying the atmosphere"—causing a specific state of mind of the masses and inducing them to act.

The most peculiar portion of the solar atmosphere is the corona. It is the outermost extension of the sun's gaseous envelope, reaching to distances of more than a million miles from the surface. It is a very tenuous gas, emitting faint light which cannot be seen in daytime because of the glare of the sun itself. During total solar eclipses, when sunlight is cut off by the interposed dark body of the moon, the corona becomes visible as a silvery aureole of indescribable beauty; often, red tongues of prominences, whose color is due to incandescent hydrogen gas, are seen rising from the solar surface into the corona. Modern spectroscopic-photographic technique makes possible the observation of the corona in daytime from elevated mountain observatories; these continuous observations, not bound to the rare and brief occasions of the eclipses, have greatly increased our knowledge about this mysterious solar phenomenon.

In the immediate neighborhood of the sun the corona consists of electrified, or *ionized,* gas, chiefly hydrogen, in which the electrons, or negatively charged particles, are knocked off the positively charged atomic nuclei and move independently in space. This electron gas, or *plasma,* has properties which greatly differ from those of ordinary gas as we know it on earth. Only the upper layers of our atmosphere, the so-called *ionosphere,* which begins at about 60 miles above the earth's surface, has similar properties (one of which is reflection of radio waves).

Most surprising is the discovery of the extremely high temperature of the corona, which reaches 1 to 2 million degrees centigrade, about 200 times higher than the sun's surface temperature. Were it not for the extreme tenuity of the coronal gas, its radiation would have annihilated everything on the earth's surface. However, the corona is extremely rarefied and therefore emits little radiation; its share in the total radiation of the sun is negligible. On the other hand, short-wave ultraviolet and X-ray radiation is emitted by the corona in noticeable quantities;

through this radiation the corona actually builds up the terrestrial ionosphere. Corpuscular radiation which causes the aurorae seems also to come chiefly from the corona, although it is initiated by happenings at a deeper level (that of sunspots). The cause of the high coronal temperature is not quite clear; it may be due partly to impact of meteoric matter from outer space, partly to turbulent disturbances (waves of moving and mixing gas) and corpuscular radiation coming from deeper layers (this radiation appears to be stopped in the corona, as it does not reach outer space). In any case, as far as solar-terrestrial relationships are concerned, from the nature of its immediate action the corona appears to be the most important portion of the solar atmosphere.

12. Heavy Light

WITH THE SOLAR ECLIPSE OF JUNE 30, 1954, IN OUR minds, we may recall one of the most sensational results of observations made on such occasions: the verification of the action of gravity upon light. The philology of the word "light" implies something not subject to gravity; yet, from the days of Newton, who thought light to consist of minute particles traveling at enormous speed, there were hints at the possibility of light, too, possessing weight, and not being an exception to the general rule which applies to what we call matter.

A stone thrown, or a bullet shot, in a horizontal direction does not move in a straight line, but, being attracted by the earth, travels along a curved path until it hits the ground; it is deflected from its original direction of motion by gravitational force. The faster-moving bullet is less deflected and travels farther than the slow stone. It was a bold idea to suggest that light, too, may be deflected by the attraction of celestial bodies. On account of its great speed, 186,000 miles a second, the deflection must be small; it would require the whole effort of such a giant body as the sun, 330,000 times more massive than the earth, to produce a small deflection, hardly perceptible with the most accurate instruments. Indeed, 150 years ago Soldner calculated that a ray of light just grazing the surface of the sun should be deflected by

0.85 seconds of arc—modern data would have led to a slightly greater figure, 0.87 seconds. This amount, which is 2,200 times smaller than the apparent diameter of the sun, is that by which the star would appear displaced outwards, away from the sun. Instead of being seen exactly on the edge of the solar disk, it would appear at a tiny distance just outside it. When the ray of light passes at a greater distance from the solar surface, the displacement is smaller; at double distance, one half; at triple distance, one third, etc. Soldner's calculation was based on Newton's theory.

The calculation remained a purely theoretical matter for over a century. It could have been verified by measuring the exact positions of stars seen near the sun during total solar eclipses, and by comparing these with the positions of the same stars at another time of the year when the sun was not in their vicinity. This was not done, undoubtedly on account of the great technical difficulties involved, which, without the help of photography, appeared to be insuperable.

The twentieth century brought Einstein's theory of relativity to improve on Newton's laws; whereas these latter remain valid so to speak in everyday life, under unusual conditions, e.g., at high velocities approaching that of light, relativity leads to different consequences. For the deflection of light by the sun, Einstein's General Theory of Relativity predicted 1.74 seconds, or exactly the double of that required by Newton's theory. The question of the precise value of the deflection became a matter of principle, enabling us to make a choice between the two physical concepts of the universe. Photography was now well developed to help the observer, and since 1919 observations have been made at total solar eclipses, to check the gravitational deflection of light by the sun. The average outcome from eight eclipses so far is 1.97 seconds for the deflection. This is certainly in favor of relativity, and is regarded as one of the observational proofs of it. Nevertheless, the figure is in excess of the predicted amount by more than could have been expected from observational errors; it may be that we do not yet know the whole story.

13. The Solar System

THE FIRST ALLEGIANCE OF THE EARTH IS TO THE SOLAR system; our globe is a little borough in the vast realm of the sun. This system is a structure of remarkable beauty which, by the regularity of the motions of its members, lent itself to the first application of precise mathematical analysis to natural phenomena. The triumph of Newton's law of gravitation in explaining, exactly describing, and predicting, the motions of the planets and their satellites, created a degree of confidence in the scientific method which never existed before. The subsequent progress of science and engineering was largely conditioned by the self-confidence gained in interpreting the motions of the celestial bodies.

Yet the success was, in the first place, due to the fact that the mass of the sun is very much (743 times) greater than that of all the planets taken together. Were there other bodies in the solar system comparable in mass with the sun, the motions of the planets would be so complicated and unpredictable that Newton's attempt would have been doomed to failure; with the means at his disposal, it would have been practically impossible for him to calculate and to predict satisfactorily the positions of the planets in the sky, although the law of gravitation would have been valid just the same.

Happily for the progress of human science, our solar system was built simply enough to be tackled with Newton's or Leibniz's calculus! But that is not the only virtue of this simplicity. In a former chapter we mentioned that in a more complicated system a planet would move erratically, without maintaining a fixed distance from its sun; in such a system life would not develop, being exterminated by alternating excessive heat and cold. Thus, without the simple structure of the solar system, there would have been neither life on earth, nor humanity, nor Newton, nor Einstein—nobody to explain the complicated courses of celestial bodies, and nobody to listen to an explanation!

The preponderance of the mass of the sun is a necessary and sufficient condition to make Newtonian "two-body" calculations successful; although also a necessary condition for the existence of life, it is not sufficient. Another prerequisite is that the orbits of the planets be approximately circular (i.e., only slightly elongated ellipses, or "of small eccentricity"), and spaced in such a manner as not to intersect, thus eliminating the danger of collision. These two conditions are also fulfilled in the solar system, at least with respect to its principal members, the major planets and their satellites. Pluto with respect to Neptune is an exception.

There are other remarkable regularities in the solar system, not directly pertaining to the conditions of life, but evidently bearing on the mode of origin of the system. These regularities can be described as follows: (a) all the planets (without exception) circle the sun in the same direction, namely, counterclockwise when observed from the northern side of the ecliptic; (b) the mutual inclinations of their orbital planes are small, most being only a few degrees (Pluto's inclination of 17° to the ecliptic is the largest, Mercury with 7° coming next; note that these largest inclinations belong to the two extreme cases —the planet farthest from, and that nearest to, the sun); (c) the distances of successive planets from the sun increase in a more or less regular progression described in *Bode's law* (Mercury, relative distance $0 + 4 = 4$; Venus, $3 + 4 = 7$; Earth, $6 + 4 = 10$; Mars, $12 + 4 = 16$; average of asteroids, $24 + 4 = 28$; Jupiter, $48 + 4 = 52$; etc.); (d) the axial rotations of the planets and the revolutions of their satellites take place generally in the same direction as that of the orbital revolutions, with a few exceptions in extreme cases (rotation and satellites of Uranus and Neptune, outer satellites of Jupiter and Saturn).

These regularities cannot be accidental. It seems that one general cause has made the wheels of the solar system turn in the same direction. This cause is to be sought in the origin of the solar system. As mentioned in Chapter 2, the old theory of nebular origin of the solar system, propounded almost two centuries ago by Kant and Laplace, is now, with some modifications, coming back into its own again, having been obscured in the meantime by other, more "modern," theories (such as the ejection of solar matter into space by tidal action of another star which happened to pass through the solar system). The main theoretical difficulty of the nebular theory, that of the *angular momentum,* is overcome by considering various processes, some of which now seem to be rather obvious. One explanation was given by the German physicist von Weizsäcker. The difficulty consisted in the slow rotation of our sun; it was argued that if the sun was formed from contraction of the same nebula which gave birth to the planets, it would have acquired a very much faster axial rotation than it actually did, with a period of a few hours instead of the observed 25 to 27 days. However, in the primordial nebula, as in every big volume of gas or liquid, there must have existed eddies and currents, whose action—the so-called "turbulent friction" or "eddy-viscosity"—slowed down the rotation of the cental portion, the sun, and pushed forward the planets, or the gaseous rings from which the planets condensed later on. Eddy-viscosity is the force which makes the entire liquid in a vessel swirl when only part of it is stirred by a spoon. This simple force, known to every housewife, was overlooked by theoretical scientists for two centuries. It is interesting to note that the eddies or vortices provide an explanation also for Bode's law: the regular spacing of planetary distances would correspond to the spacing of major eddies in the solar nebula, the more distant eddies being bigger than those nearer the center.

More recently it has been pointed out that electromagnetic interaction between the sun and the surrounding gas, and especially the action of interstellar magnetic fields in the past, was amply sufficient to reduce the speed of rotation of the sun to its present value. Thus, the angular-momentum difficulty no longer exists, and there is little doubt left that the solar system originated from the contraction of a rotating nebula. The nebula contained gas and dust. Its speed of rotation increased with contraction, and a flattened shape (due to centrifugal force) was acquired. Dust condensed into greater and greater lumps, forming the nuclei of the sun and planets. The sun lost its excessive rotational speed by the combined action of turbulent friction and magnetic forces; at the same time it contracted into its present volume and sucked up most of the gaseous constituents of the nebula. Through contraction the sun became extremely hot, and the dust substance was completely vaporized. The smaller planets were chiefly built of the dust, which, after compression and melting, became solid rock; their gravitational pull was insufficient to collect the gas from surrounding space. The large planets— Jupiter, Saturn, Uranus, Neptune—were able to attract the gas, and their composition is similar to that of the sun, hydrogen and helium being their chief constituents.

One need not think that the solar system came into being at once with its present regular shape. The directions of revolution and rotation were probably more or less the same as they are now, and the orbital inclinations small, the planetary orbits being confined to the vicinity of the equatorial plane of the original nebula. On the other hand, many orbits must have been elongated, with many stray bodies of various sizes intersecting one another's paths. This led to collisions, and after a few million years most of the trespassers were eliminated, the smaller bodies being absorbed by the larger planets. Only those planets remained which did not interfere with one another's orbits. Thus, the present regular spacing of the planetary orbits is, to some extent, a product of natural selection. Even now, not all stray bodies have disappeared, especially in the more distant portions of the solar system where motions are slow and longer time intervals are required for elimination by collisions. Comets, meteors, and the asteroids are examples of such stray bodies, remnants of the primordial chaos. When a shooting star flares up in the darkness of the night sky, it reminds us of a time when the universe was young and the solar system was in the making, when billions of shooting stars covered the sky with an incessant glare, heating up the surface of the growing earthball to the temperature of molten lava.

The accompanying table contains a few numerical data referring to the sun and planets which form the essence of the solar system. There may be planets beyond Neptune and Pluto, not yet discovered because of their distance and faintness. In addition to the planets, the solar system is filled with a swarm of much smaller bodies which roam its space everywhere and in all directions:

THE SOLAR SYSTEM

NAME	SUN	MERCURY	VENUS	EARTH	MARS	ASTEROIDS	JUPITER	SATURN	URANUS	NEPTUNE	PLUTO
Diameter (Earth=1)	109	0.39	0.97	1	0.53	0.07 to 0.0001	11.2	9.2	3.9	4.2	1.?
Mass (Earth=1)	333,000	0.06	0.82	1	0.11	0.001*	318.	95.	15.	17.	0.1–0.8?
Relative distance from sun	0	0.387	0.723	1	1.524	2.8**	5.20	9.54	19.2	30.0	39.5
Period of revolution, years	—	0.241	0.615	1	1.88	4.7**	11.9	29.5	84.	165.	248.
Period of axial rotation, days	25–27	88	137	1	1.03	0.2 to 0.5	0.41	0.43	0.45	0.53	6.39
Number of known satellites	...	0	0	1	2	...	12	9	5	2	0
Ideal temperature, surface, °C	5,500	188	66	15	−39	−101	−147	−180	−207	−220	−227

* Total mass of all asteroids.
**Typical distance and period of revolution.

these are the meteors and the comets. Their sizes vary from a few miles in diameter down to the smallest particles of dust. Their number is very great—it is believed that comets alone number about 100,000 million (mostly confined to the farthest outskirts of the solar system); the meteors are almost numberless, but their total mass hardly exceeds that of the earth, which is negligible as compared with the mass of the solar system. In terms of mass, these stray bodies are unimportant. When considering the main features of the solar system, we may rightly forget about them, and content ourselves with considering only the sun and the planets.

The last line of the table gives the "ideal temperature" in degrees centigrade. Except for the sun, this indicates the average temperature of the surface of each body, provided that its atmospheric properties, reflecting power for sunlight, and axial rotation are the same as those of our earth. The true temperatures may in some cases differ considerably from these values, but in general the tabular temperatures give a fair idea of the degree of heat or cold on the planets. Thus, there is no doubt that on all planets farther than Mars, or over the major portion of the solar system, there reigns intense cold; compared with this cold, our polar winter would seem like summer heat. Temperatures of terrestrial range occur only within the narrow belt between Mars and Venus; Mercury is too hot, at least on its sunlit side.

Of the planets, five are visible to the naked eye and have been known since ancient times: Mercury, Venus, Mars, Jupiter, and Saturn. Uranus was discovered by Sir William Herschel in 1781. Neptune was found in 1846 by Galle near the position predicted mathematically by Le Verrier and Adams from perturbations of Uranus; Neptune betrayed its existence by the gravitational pull which it exerted on its neighbor. Pluto was discovered in 1930 in a similar manner by Tombaugh, near the position calculated by Lowell, also from perturbations of Uranus. The first minor planet, Ceres, was discovered in 1801 by Piazzi, and since then nearly 2,000 asteroids have been registered. Between Mars and Jupiter there must be millions of them, the majority too small to be observed. Ceres, with a diameter of nearly 500 miles, is the largest among the asteroids; its mass is about

1/4,000 of that of the earth, and about ¼ the mass of all the asteroids together. Clearly, as compared with the principal planets, the asteroids are insignificant and should more properly be classified with the stray bodies. Most probably they represent the result of a collision between two ancient planets.

Mercury, the smallest of all the principal planets and the nearest to the sun, has no atmosphere. Its period of axial rotation, 88 days, equals that of its revolution around the sun. The cause of this equality is the tidal force of the sun, which forced Mercury to turn one side to its ruler. Therefore, the illuminated side, under permanent solar radiation and unprotected by an atmosphere, has an almost red-hot temperature of about 400°C, at which lead would melt. The dark side never sees sunlight and is at a temperature not much above absolute zero, about –240°C; it would be lower still but for the small amount of internal heat which undoubtedly Mercury possesses, as does the earth and every planet containing radioactive substances. In any case, it seems that the dark side of Mercury is the coldest place in the solar system. How strange that the coldest spot is found on the planet nearest to the sun!

Venus has an atmosphere at least as thick as the terrestrial, with great amounts of carbonic acid gas, but apparently devoid of oxygen and water vapor. Clouds of dust conceal its surface, of which we know nothing. The period of axial rotation is not known, but judging from indirect data it may be about 10 to 30 days, around an axis inclined 20° to 30° to the plane of the orbit.

Mars is the most popular planet because of the possibility of some life on its surface. It has a thin atmosphere, with a little water vapor and a considerable quantity of carbonic acid gas. Its two tiny moons, about 10 and 5 miles in diameter, revolve quite close to the surface of the planet: the nearer in 7½ hours, overtaking the rotation of the planet which is 24½ hours; it thus rises in the west and sets in the east at least twice a day! The more distant, smaller moon revolves in 30½ hours, slowly overtaken by the planet's rotation and, thus, rising and setting in the "usual" quarters.

Jupiter, the largest planet, has twelve known moons and is the center of a system which, in miniature, imitates the solar system. However, only four moons are of considerable size, about equal to or slightly bigger than our moon, the rest being small bodies of the size of small asteroids, and thus insignificant. Jupiter is a gaseous body without a solid surface.

Saturn, the next biggest planet, is also gaseous and has a numerous retinue of satellites—nine are at present known. Of these, only one exceeds our moon in size; the rest are smaller, although seven of them are considerably greater than Jupiter's small satellites. The rings of Saturn distinguish this planet from all others; they consist of fragments, formed in the place of a broken-up or never-born satellite, which were prevented from gathering into one body by the tidal force of the planet.

Uranus and Neptune, almost twins, complete the list of the four giant outer planets. They are apparently gaseous, as are their major brothers Jupiter and Saturn. These four planets consist largely of hydrogen and helium, with an admixture of other gases such as methane and ammonia which are observed in the outer layers. Carbon dioxide and water vapor are undoubtedly also present but, because of the low temperature of the surface, they must have become frozen there and sunk toward deeper layers (exactly as water vapor behaves in the terrestrial atmosphere). Free oxygen must be absent, otherwise it would combine with hydrogen, forming water. Each of the four outer planets may have a relatively small rocky or iron core. These cores, from 10,000 to 35,000 miles beneath the planetary surface, would be subject to pressures of many millions of atmospheres, at temperatures of several thousand degrees. Under such conditions they could not be the seat of life. In spite of the internal heat, little heat reaches the surface. Even Jupiter's internal heat does not contribute appreciably to the temperature of its surface, which, according to measurements, disposes only of the small amount of radiation that reaches it from the sun. Therefore the surfaces of the four outer planets are terribly cold, the temperatures differing little from those given in the last line of the table.

Pluto's surface is so cold that terrestrial air would freeze there into snowflakes. However, the dark side of Mercury is even colder. On the other hand, Pluto is too small to hold firmly the light gases, hydrogen and helium. To all appearance, Pluto is a solid rocky body like our earth; it could be similar to our globe but for the extremely low surface temperature.

Of all the major planets, Pluto alone violates the rule of noninterference with its neighbors. Its orbit crosses that of Neptune, and although at present the two orbits do not intersect, planetary perturbations may lead in time to a true intersection. Therefore, Pluto is in a most dangerous position with respect to Neptune; this may end either in a collision or in the expulsion of Pluto from the solar system. The possibilities will be considered in a later chapter.

14. The Evening Star

FROM THE VERY DAWN OF HUMAN TRADITION VESPER, the Evening Star, has attracted the attention of mankind more than any other star in the sky. Because of its extreme brightness—in the night sky the brilliance of this planet is exceeded only by the moon—it stands out in the twilight, when other bright planets and stars are but dimly visible. The only rival of Vesper was Lucifer, "the one who brings the light," or the Morning Star; in fact, even nowadays it is widely believed that the evening star and morning star are two distinct objects. However, even in antiquity it soon became clear to those concerned with astronomical observations that both names referred to the same object, a wandering star or planet which the Romans called Venus. The name given to it was that of the goddess of love, in which respect the Romans followed the traditions of more ancient people. By its peaceful golden-white luster, embedded in the colorful glory of the twilight after sunset, it struck the romantic imagination and associated itself with the tender side of human nature.

Being closer to the sun, Venus moves faster than the earth and overtakes it from time to time; it may be seen sometimes to the east, sometimes to the west of the sun, appearing thus alternately as the Evening and the Morning Star. When changing over from evening to morning, the planet passes between sun and earth, a configuration called *inferior conjunction.*

The period of revolution, or the year of Venus, is 7½ months; its period of axial rotation is probably long, in the neighborhood of 10 to 30 days. According to recent photographic studies, the inclination of the planet's equator to the orbital plane is about the same as for the earth.

A short year with a long day makes the climatic conditions on Venus very different from those on earth. Because of the length of the day the diurnal range in temperature should be comparable to the greatest differences between terrestrial summer and winter. The axial inclination would increase these differences by causing seasonal variation as on earth.

The distance of Venus from the sun is only 67 million miles, against 93 million miles for the earth. Therefore, Venus receives from the sun almost double the amount of heat that our globe gets. Although covered with thick clouds which considerably weaken the solar heat, the surface temperature of the sunlit side of Venus must be extremely hot, about 130°F, whereas the temperature of the dark side may drop to near freezing point, around 30°F. Between these two extremes, especially in the polar regions, there are places where temperature conditions might be acceptable to visitors from the earth.

Direct measurements of temperature give a very low apparent value, about −27°F, for Venus; this, however, refers to the cloud layer at the top of the atmosphere, and the surface, which cannot be observed, must be very much warmer. Besides, the apparent value does not allow for the "emissivity" of the Venusian clouds, whose true temperature is considerably higher.

In inferior conjunction important physical observations of the planet can be made. Venus at this time turns its "back," i.e., its nonilluminated hemisphere, toward the terrestrial observer; the situation is similar to that at new moon, and the planet should become invisible. However, by observing the planet with a telescope near inferior conjunction, it was long ago discovered that, far from becoming invisible, it shows a bright rim or narrow illuminated border extending over more than one-half of the circumference; the horns of the "new moon" of Venus extend over the semicircle, their ends sometimes even merging into one another and producing a complete illuminated ring around the dark invisible hemisphere of the planet. No such phenomenon is observed with the moon. These extended "horns" indicate that Venus is surrounded by a noticeable atmosphere which reflects and scatters sunlight in the same manner as the terrestrial atmosphere. Our atmosphere remains visible after sunset, its upper portions still illuminated while the earth's surface is already merged into darkness; the most beautiful scenery on earth is caused by this twilight illumination. The prolongation of the cusps of the narrow crescent of Venus near inferior conjunction is also a twilight effect; thus, on Venus the succession of day and night is softened by twilight, making gradual the transition between light and darkness, exactly as it is at dusk and dawn on earth. It is quite unlike the moon, where bright sunlight changes abruptly into black, colorless darkness the moment the edge of the solar disk disappears below the horizon.

Thus, Venus possesses an atmosphere; the size and the mass of the planet, as well as its surface gravity, differ little from our own abode, and there seems to be enough similarity to call Venus our sister planet.

Until quite recently there was a widespread belief that, compared with the other planets, the conditions of life on Venus might be most similar to those on earth. Being closer to the sun, Venus should enjoy a much warmer climate. Therefore romantic stories of interplanetary adventure were written, describing tropical landscapes with luxurious vegetation, monstrous animals and a human population of various qualities, according to the imagination and taste of the writer. Modern research has led to a much less attractive picture of the conditions on Venus.

Although it hides its face underneath a thick layer of clouds which jealously conceal the features of its surface, this planet betrays its true nature through the composition of its atmosphere. There exists an extended atmosphere; but, according to spectroscopic evidence, oxygen, our source of life, is absent, and water vapor can be present only in very small quantities, if at all. Recent observations of an auroral display on Venus seem to indicate the presence of nitrogen and confirm the absence of oxygen. On the other hand, carbonic acid gas, the product of burning on earth and the chief substance exhaled by animals, is present on Venus in quantities comparable to those of oxygen in the terrestrial atmosphere.

We inhale oxygen and exhale carbonic acid gas; in the atmosphere of Venus we could not live, nor could any other terrestrial animal. Of course, plants thrive on carbonic acid gas; they absorb it, retaining carbon and setting free the oxygen. Might it not be possible that plants grow on Venus? The answer is—they could, provided there is water. However, if plants covered the surface of Venus as thickly as they do the surface of the earth, practically all the carbonic acid gas would have been absorbed by them within a few hundred thousand years and converted into oxygen. The planet Venus has existed for thousands of millions of years, and even a much sparser population of plants than ours would long ago have resulted in the creation of an oxygen-containing atmosphere. A similar process must undoubtedly have taken place at the dawn of life on earth, our atmospheric oxygen being mainly a product of the activity of our vegetation. The absence of oxygen is a definite proof of the absence of extensive vegetation, and thus of life as we know it, on Venus.

Venus is apparently a dead planet; the reason why life has not started there may be the absence, or scarcity, of free water. The clouds which perpetually cover the whole of its sunlit hemisphere would, if such is the case, consist of the finest dust, produced by the grinding of rocks and sand, then blown about by the winds and carried everywhere high into the atmosphere. In the absence of water, the dust would be much more loose and free to fly around than on earth. The modern picture of Venus as a borderless desert, extending over an area one hundred times that of Sahara, and swept by a dusty choking atmosphere at 130°F, is much less inviting than that drawn from fantastic dreams of old. Sahara itself would appear a paradise compared with the dry and suffocating dust storms raging behind the brilliant deceitful face of the Evening Star.

There have been recent attempts to explain away the failure of the spectroscope to reveal water vapor on

Venus, and to suggest that the visible clouds of this planet consist of water or ice at such a low temperature that little water vapor would remain above them. These attempts are not convincing. The strongest argument against such suggestions is the color of Venus: it is definitely yellow, as compared with the bluish color of the earth (the color being measured photometrically, in the case of the earth from the earthshine on the dark side of the moon). Therefore, the composition of the Venusian clouds must be very different from that of terrestrial clouds; the latter being composed of water, the clouds of Venus cannot be water.

15.　Mars

MUCH HAS BEEN WRITTEN ABOUT MARS, AND IT IS OFTEN so controversial that the impression gained by the lay reader who comes across the Martian literature may be rather confused. This state of affairs does not do justice to our knowledge of the red planet. Actually, there exists a wealth of well-established facts which an experienced observer would be able to ascertain during one observational season with the aid of a relatively small telescope. We will therefore introduce our description with a typical series of observations—those obtained by the writer in 1952 with a 10-inch refractor.

In that year Mars, as observed from Armagh Observatory, presented its usual aspect. In May the Martian season corresponded to our beginning of August, thus to summer well advanced in the northern hemisphere of Mars, and to winter in the southern hemisphere. Around the North Pole there was visible a white polar cap, relatively small as befitted the season. The polar caps of Mars apparently consist of snow or hoarfrost which deposits on the ground during the long cold nights of winter and melts or evaporates in summer. Therefore, in summer only a small region, close around the pole, remains covered with permanent snow or ice that does not melt, such as was observed in the present case. In winter vast regions are covered with the white deposit; the observations of 1952 showed a whitish haze in the southern hemisphere of Mars, which might have been the winter snow or the clouds from which the snow is deposited. Except at the poles, the snow sheet must be generally very thin, perhaps a few inches only, otherwise it would not disappear so quickly in the spring sun.

The polar caps are almost the only indication of the existence of water on Mars. There is very little water indeed, all of it in the form either of vapor suspended in the atmosphere or of snow and ice collected around the poles. It is certain that no open water surfaces exist on Mars, at least not in its equatorial or tropical regions—not even a small lake or pond. A water surface would reveal itself sometimes by glittering, caused by a reflection of the solar image which would occasionally flash up as a bright spot; such a phenomenon has never been observed on Mars. In the polar regions, during the melting of the snow, a dark fringe around the polar cap sometimes appears (it was not visible in May, 1952, but was observed from Armagh in 1950). This may be true liquid water; however, it does not last long.

In addition to the polar white areas, a bright whitish spot was observed several times in 1952 near the Martian equator at sunset, disappearing in daytime; this may have been haze, or hoarfrost. As compared with the earth, Mars is farther away and gets less heat from the sun; therefore, the mean temperature at the Martian equator may be near zero Fahrenheit, or about that of Siberia or Northern Canada. The diurnal range of temperature must be very great, because of little protection from the atmosphere: from 60°F in daytime to –60°F at night. If, nevertheless, snow there is a rare occurrence, it is not because of lack of cold, but because of the extreme dryness of the atmosphere, which does not favor precipitation.

The Martian dark areas, called *maria,* surrounded by the orange-yellow *continentes* were clearly visible in 1952 as the planet rotated, turning its different portions to the terrestrial observer.

The period of rotation of Mars is 24 hours 37 minutes, and the inclination of its axis 23°; both figures are close to the corresponding values for our earth. The length of the Martian day and the succession of the seasons on Mars are very similar to ours, and this has induced many optimistic minds to dream of a life on Mars, built on a more or less terrestrial pattern. Our present knowledge is certainly discouraging from this standpoint. Mars is a desert, drier than Sahara and colder than Siberia. Its *maria,* although devoid of water, may be tundralike plains, covered with a strange vegetation of mosses or lichens; its *continentes,* covering the major part of the planet, are deserts where dust clouds are sometimes raised by the whirlwinds. The almost complete absence of oxygen makes the planet quite unacceptable to human beings.

If life exists on Mars, it must be adapted to stern conditions of which there is not the like on earth. As compared with Mars, the desert sands of Sahara or the glaciers of the Antarctic would appear to us as a welcome place of repose. Only the dead surface of the moon, staring into a vacuum, or the hell of a Venusian dust storm may be worse. Martian plants have to undergo daily a cycle of alternating growth and frozen stupor which terrestrial plants in temperate climates follow in the course of a year. Martian plants would be frozen hard at night; in the morning, when warmed up by the sunrays, they must be able to come quickly to life and continue the growth interrupted by the nocturnal cold. They would have to be *hygroscopic,* or able to protect their water from evaporation in daytime when the air is extremely dry. As to the supply of moisture, it cannot come from the completely dry soil. The only imaginable supply is hoarfrost, depositing at night, of which the plants must be able somehow to catch a few precious drops when it melts in the morning—and quickly, before it evaporates into the desert air. From this standpoint it appears that the extreme nocturnal cold is a blessing which might make life on Mars possible; in its dry air, a moderate cold, such as is encountered at night on earth, would never cause a deposition of moisture from the atmosphere.

The conditions on Mars are so severe that time and again doubts have been expressed as to the possibility of life on that planet. Quite recently a theory has been advanced that ascribes the dark areas on Mars and their seasonal variation to deposits of volcanic ashes, and to changes of color of a chemical nature. There are, however, too many inconsistencies in the theory to make it acceptable. The best explanation still seems to be that the dark areas are covered with vegetation. This is supported not only by the seasonal character of the changes in the dark areas, which obviously respond to the advent of warmth in spring, and of moisture provided by the melting polar cap. An even stronger argument in favor of the organic nature of the dark areas is that if the difference between the dark and bright markings on Mars were similar to that on the moon, implying dead areas of different shading and coloration, the dust storms raging there from time to time (and actually observed in the form of yellow clouds) would long ago have done away with it. After the passage of millions of centuries everything on Mars would be covered by a sheet of yellow sand and dust, perhaps a mile thick, concealing the differences in shading. The possibility of continuous chemical modification of the depositing dust, say, by hygroscopic salt layers covering the surface of the *maria,* must be rejected because no such surface could withstand the incessant pouring in of deposits for such enormous intervals of time. Organic life, probably in the form of vegetation that defies the sand drifts and feeds on the dust, appears to be the only explanation.

Why, then, does vegetation develop in some regions and not in others, while the entire surface of Mars (except the poles) seems to be uniformly dry? The dark areas, or *maria,* appear to be depressions on the surface of Mars; being at a lower level, and absorbing more sunrays because of their darker coloration, they should be warmer than the rest of the surface. Direct radiometric measurements of the temperature of different portions of the Martian surface confirm this suggestion. There may also be some possibility of accumulation of ground water in the depressions. This, with the warmer climate, may have made the depressions a preferential seat of life. Nevertheless, fainter dark markings, of a depth of shade varying according to season, are observed everywhere on the *continentes*. This would indicate that, if there are really plants on Mars, they are to be found thinly scattered all over its surface, the *maria* being only more thickly covered by them. The appearance of vast darkish areas on former "continental" spaces, as observed in 1954, is consistent with this view.

Single plants separated by areas of barren soil may be the type of vegetation on Mars, as it is on terrestrial semideserts (for example, inside the Grand Canyon of the Colorado River and on the Arizona Plateau).

The Martian atmosphere contains carbonic acid gas, which would enable plants to breathe there in the same way as on earth. Carbonic acid gas is the only constituent of the Martian atmosphere which has been detected spectroscopically; its amount is somewhat greater than in the terrestrial atmosphere, but still relatively small. Water vapor is the other constituent definitely present. The rest of the atmosphere probably consists of nitrogen, with some argon; these gases are not detectable under ordinary conditions. The density of the Martian atmosphere at ground level is about 8 per cent of the terrestrial—so low, indeed, that human beings could not walk there freely even when supplied with oxygen. The density is equal to that at an altitude of about 14 miles on earth. The pressure of the Martian atmosphere is near the limit at which human blood would boil; the blood would fill the lungs and cause death. Therefore, visitors from earth, if they ever land on Mars, will have to be enclosed in airtight pressurized suits and carry their oxygen with them. On the other hand, the temperature conditions on Mars are not so prohibitive for human beings as they are on Venus or the moon.

If there are plants on Mars, why do they not produce a perceptible amount of oxygen? One possible explanation is that the Martian atmosphere is so thin that solar ultraviolet radiation would penetrate it to a deeper level than on earth. This radiation converts oxygen into ozone (the gas responsible for the peculiar smell after electric discharges or lightning), which is chemically very active and probably combines with the surface material on Mars. On earth the ozone layer, at an altitude around 25 miles, is kept from direct contact with the earth's surface; this has saved the oxygen of our atmosphere from disappearing, and us from poisoning—because ozone is poisonous. On Mars, the oxygen would quickly disappear; however, small amounts of it may still be present there.

Another explanation is that, in the Martian upper atmosphere, molecular oxygen is broken up into atomic oxygen (as happens in the terrestrial ionosphere), which is so light that it escapes to space.

We have not yet said a word about the "canals" of Mars. This phenomenon, which has been so much talked about, has been given undue importance. The canals belong to the network of faint dark markings which we mentioned before, and which covers the whole surface of Mars. Although there is no doubt about the existence of such markings, they may not be as regular as is suggested by some students of Mars. Rows of irregular dark spots may appear as straight lines under difficult conditions of observation. Nevertheless, such lines—whether continuous or consisting of chains of spots—undoubtedly exist; the question of whether or not they are perfectly straight is irrelevant. On the other hand, there is no good reason to assume that the canal network is the product of activity of intelligent beings. They may be rifts or cracks in the surface layers or crust, favoring the growth of vegetation which makes them visible. The impact of asteroids, which are numerous in the vicinity of Mars, may have caused these cracks; the divergence of several canals from one center—a more conspicuous dark spot— is suggestive of cracks in a windowpane, produced by a bullet or a stone missile.

As to the hypothesis of Martian inhabitants—intelligent beings—it is not only unfounded, but extremely improbable. With the low pressure of the Martian atmosphere, warm-blooded animals could not exist there; the practical absence of oxygen makes the presence of any kind of animal life improbable. It is true that life can adapt itself to extreme conditions, by gradual "training," i.e., by the elimination of the weak and survival of the fittest. For that, however, one must have some reasonable living conditions to begin with; on Mars, such conditions may never have existed. Nevertheless, we do not know everything about life, and should therefore be cautious about finally dismissing Mars as uninhabitable.

16. Jupiter

WHEN THE ANCIENTS LINKED THE NAME OF THIS PLANET with the chief god of their Olympus, the choice was hardly accidental. The slow apparent motion of Jupiter was suggestive of a relatively great distance, whereas its great brilliance, in spite of the distance, indicated a size larger than that of all the other "wandering stars," members of the solar system, except the sun itself. The instinctive belief of the ancients has been well confirmed by modern observations.

Jupiter is the largest planet. Although a dwarf as compared with the sun, the "King of the Planets" exceeds the earth 11 times in diameter, 1,300 times in volume, but only 318 times in weight (mass). The comparison of mass with volume indicates that Jupiter is made of much lighter stuff than our planet. In fact, the average density of Jupiter is only 1.3 times, whereas the density of the earth is 5.5 times, that of water. With such a low density, Jupiter cannot be composed of solid rock, at least not in its outer portions. Indeed, observations suggest that the outer portions of this planet, those accessible to the astronomer's eye, are gaseous, without the least indication of a solid crust underneath. There are clouds suspended in this atmosphere which, because of the fast rotation, are lined up parallel to the equator, forming the well-known bands of Jupiter, visible in the smallest telescopes. The bands and various other cloudy formations indicate a period of rotation of 9 hours 55 minutes, which, together with the larger size of the planet, leads to a speed of rotation 27 times that of the earth. An equatorial band rotates even faster, with a period of 9 hours 50 minutes. The different periods of revolution would not, of course, be possible in a solid body.

The atmosphere of Jupiter contains methane and ammonia, which have been identified only recently, although the presence of the corresponding spectral bands was known long ago, their interpretation remaining a riddle for almost half a century. These gases can persist only in an atmosphere rich in hydrogen and devoid of oxygen, otherwise they would be converted into carbonic acid gas and water vapor in the hot inner portions of the atmosphere, or even exploded at the impact of meteors. The temperature of the clouds of Jupiter's atmosphere is very low, −220°F from direct measurements; this is about what should be expected if solar radiation is the chief source of heat and if little comes from the interior of the planet. A similar case is that of our earth, which has to rely on solar radiation alone to maintain life on its surface. But Jupiter is 5.2 times farther away and gets 27 times less heat from the sun than we do; hence the extremely low temperature. The lowest temperatures of the Siberian winter are tropical heat in comparison with the temperature of the visible surface of Jupiter. No doubt the temperature increases inwards, and at a considerable depth it may reach hundreds, even thousands, of degrees; these hot regions are, however, concealed beneath the immense depth of the outer, colder layers, and no perceptible radiation from them comes to the surface. In old days Jupiter was often spoken of as a little sun, almost red-hot and radiating enough heat to maintain life on its satellites; this vision is now certainly proved to be untrue. Jupiter's satellites are as cold as the surface of Jupiter itself, and cannot be seats of life on a terrestrial pattern.

Jupiter is a strange world, far too different from our own abode of life to offer any attractions to earthly visitors, except the satisfying of scientific curiosity or a longing for knowledge. There is little doubt that in the not too distant future (astronomically speaking, i.e., within thousands of years from now) rocket ships from earth will dash through the spaces of the solar system, primarily with the purpose of solving riddles which astronomy from our present position in space is unable to solve. A return journey to Jupiter would take about 10 years. However, the first explorers will hardly risk a landing on the frozen plains of Jupiter's moons, nor will they land on Jupiter itself. Such a landing would mean a number of dangers—first of being poisoned by the gases of Jupiter's atmosphere; then, of being frozen to death; of being crushed by the force of gravity, which is 2.7 times the terrestrial; and finally, in the absence of solid landing ground, of going down "straight to hell," to the interior hot regions.

Jupiter has recently been in the news by reason of the radio-noise which it has been found to emit sometimes. The noise is apparently due to electric discharges, or thunderstorms, connected with certain definite spots visible on its surface.

17. The Rings of Saturn

ANYONE IN POSSESSION OF A SMALL TELESCOPE CAN avail himself of the opportunity to observe the greatest wonder of the solar system—Saturn's rings. In the equatorial plane of the planet a system of perfectly circular rings stretches out from 9,000 to 47,000 miles from the surface of Saturn, whose diameter is 75,000 miles or almost ten times that of the earth. There are three principal rings; the outer two brilliantly shining in reflected sunlight and separated by a narrow space, and the third, an inner "gray" ring conspicuous only where it passes over the sunlit disk of Saturn as a dark band. The sight is so strange that the first observers, with rather imperfect telescopes, did not believe their eyes and thought they were seeing three separate bodies—Saturn's disk in the middle and a large satellite on each side.

To the present-day astronomer the rings of Saturn are much less of a puzzle. In fact, the ring-shaped arrangement of matter plays a conspicuous role in the theories of the origin of the solar system. It is believed that, in the nebulous cloud from which our solar system originated, the diffuse matter condensed into several rings; later on, each ring condensed into a planet. The satellites of the planets may have been formed in a similar manner, from nebulous or dust rings attached to each planet. All but one of the original rings of the solar system have disappeared; only Saturn's rings remain as a living testimony of the old days of creation.

What prevented the rings of Saturn from condensing into one or several satellites, to join the company of the known nine and the probable host of small unknown satellites of that planet? The answer is—Saturn itself, by virtue of tidal force. The tidal force, like that exercised by the moon on the earth, produces an unequal gravitational pull; the moon attracts more strongly the nearer parts of the earth and pulls them away from the farther parts which are less strongly attracted; a disruptive or distending force results which, in the case of the lunar tides, is too weak to affect appreciably the solid rocky shell of the earth, and succeeds only in moving slightly the liquid on its surface, producing the ocean tides. Saturn is 95 times heavier than the earth, or 7,600 times more massive than the moon, and the rings are much nearer to Saturn's surface than the moon is to the earth. A satellite placed at the distance of its rings from Saturn would be subject to an enormous tidal force, sufficient to tear it to pieces even were it made of solid rock. The rings are too close to Saturn for the formation of a satellite.

By its tidal force Saturn has prevented matter from being collected into one single body. From the high reflecting power of the bright rings, similar to that of snow, and from certain spectroscopic evidence, it appears probable that the rings consist of ice crystals or snowflakes into which a water-vapor envelope condensed at a time when the solar system came into being. Each of these snowflakes revolves around Saturn on its own orbit, like a tiny satellite; they are tightly packed, one beside another, occasionally "elbowing" one another, thus producing friction. This friction has caused the rings to become regular circular disks of an extremely small thickness; the thickness is equal to the average diameter of one particle only, perhaps a few inches, or even less. In any case, although the actual thickness of the rings is unknown, it cannot be more than about 1,000 feet, otherwise the rings would have influenced, by their gravitation, the motion of Saturn's satellites. No such influence has ever been observed.

18. Pluto

SIX PRINCIPAL PLANETS HAVE BEEN KNOWN SINCE ANcient times; these, all visible to the naked eye, are Mercury, Venus, Earth, Mars, Jupiter, and Saturn. With the discovery of the telescope, and later with the application of photography, three additions to the list were made in the course of the past two centuries. These were: Uranus, accidentally discovered by Sir William Herschel in 1781; Neptune, discovered theoretically by Le Verrier and Adams, and first identified in 1846 by Galle, at the Berlin Observatory; and Pluto, predicted theoretically by Lowell in 1915, but actually found on a photographic plate by Tombaugh at Lowell Observatory in Arizona fifteen years later, when Dr. Percival Lowell, the discoverer of the new planet and the founder of the observatory bearing his name, no longer trod the paths of this world.

After Neptune, Pluto was the second case of a planet being discovered not by watching the sky directly, but by calculations. From certain irregularities in the motion of another planet, Uranus, Lowell concluded that somewhere out in space there must be an unknown body which by its attraction produced the above-mentioned irregularities, or *perturbations*. Lowell was able to indicate the direction in which the new body, already called Pluto, should be visible. Owing to the faintness of the object (it turned out to be 4,000 times fainter than the faintest stars visible to the naked eye), the search took a considerable time, whence the gap of fifteen years between prediction and identification.

Pluto is the farthest planet of the solar system; its average distance from the sun is 39 times that of the earth, whereas for Neptune the corresponding figure is 30. Although Pluto moves mostly outside the orbit of Neptune, its orbit is rather elongated and the planet may sometimes be inside Neptune's orbit. This is the only case in the solar system where the paths of two large planets may cross. At present the two orbits do not intersect. However, planetary perturbations affect the orbits in such a manner that once in a while, say, once in a few million years, intersection may take place. Therefore, a collision of Pluto with Neptune may happen in the remote future, but the chances are so small that such a catastrophe may not take place for, say, 10,000 million years, or a time interval two to three times the age of the solar system. Humanity will probably never be witness to such a collision.

It is more probable that, at a close approach to Neptune, the orbit of Pluto may be altered in such a manner as to cross the orbits of Uranus and Saturn and, as a further step, even that of Jupiter. These planets, through their gravitational action at encounter, will be able to eject Pluto from the solar system, as an alternative to a possibility of collision. It appears that Pluto's chances of being removed from the solar system are such that one cannot guarantee its presence for more than 200 million years. This is a short period as compared with the age of the solar system. Similarly, it is improbable that Pluto has been near its present orbit for more than 200 million years, or one-twentieth of the age of the solar system. Apparently, Pluto is a "newcomer" and may have arrived at its present position from other regions of space.

It may be added that all the other large planets are safe with respect to mutual interference, their orbits never intersecting; they always keep out of one another's path.

The "insecurity" of Pluto's position is, however, not the only remarkable feature attached to this planet. There exists an unexplained contradiction between the determination of its mass and the observations of its size. According to careful analysis, a mass of Pluto about equal to that of the earth would be required to account for the observed perturbations in the motion of Uranus. Direct observations with the 200-inch telescope at Mount Palomar indicated a diameter of less than 4,000 miles, or a volume only about one tenth of that of the earth. The mass corresponding to so small a volume could not explain the perturbations of Uranus.

Were the density of Pluto ten times the density of the earth, or about three times that of gold, the discrepancy would be removed. It is true that some self-luminous stars have indeed such, and larger, densities, but the cause of the large density of these abnormal stars is known—it requires, in the first place, a large mass, perhaps 100,000 times the mass of the earth. In the case of a small mass like Pluto, the compression by its own gravity is unable to produce in ordinary matter a density exceeding ten times that of water. The possibility of an extremely high density for Pluto must be ruled out.

Another possibility is that the determination of the diameter may be subject to an unknown source of error. First of all, even with the largest telescopes Pluto is a difficult object, and the impression of its diameter may be spurious. It has been suggested that Pluto has a smooth, mirrorlike surface. Experiments with polished metal spheres have shown that such a reflecting "bullet," when observed from a distance, may appear less than one half its true size on account of reflection effects which make the center appear bright and the edge almost invisible. Pluto may be covered with an ocean of liquid air (Pluto's temperature is about 370°F below zero) or some other substance which lies smooth under the arctic calm and reflects sunlight like a steel ball, producing a false impression about its actual size.

As a third possibility, one could suspect that the perturbations of Uranus, considered by Lowell, were caused not by Pluto, but by another, larger body which remained undiscovered. The calculations gave only the approximate direction in which the perturbing planet was to be sought. It may be that the discovery of Pluto was a coincidence, and that the true cause of the perturbations is another planet, still farther away from the sun.

Pluto shows a variation in brightness which has persisted over several years, and can be explained by rotation of the planet. The rotation is slow, the period being equal to about 6½ days. The variation in the intensity of its light would correspond to spots of unequal brightness on a solid surface, like those on the moon or Mars, turning around and alternately appearing and disappearing as the planet rotates. Irregularities which would be caused by cloud formations are not observed. The smoothness of the variations does not support the hypothesis of mirrorlike reflection, which would show rather sudden changes in brightness.

Thus, different observations seem to lead to contradictory conclusions, but some of the discrepancies may be due to errors which are inherent in the observations of this distant and faint planet. However, the conflicting results will not discourage astronomers, who will repeat their efforts until the riddle of Pluto is solved.

19. The Comets

COMETS, VAGABONDS OF CELESTIAL SPACE, HAVE IMpressed the imagination of mankind since time immemorial. Their unusual shape—with a "hairy" head and a luminous tail like a sword, so very different from other celestial bodies, and their unexpected appearance and disappearance—filled the spectator with superstitious fear. Their motion, which did not follow the simple regularities shown by the planets, was a puzzle to the ancients.

Comets move in highly eccentric or elongated orbits, quite unlike the planetary orbits which they are crossing, heedless of "safety regulations." However, the law of gravitation accounts for this motion, and in modern times, beginning with Newton, the motion of the comets has ceased to be a major mystery; they obey the same law of gravitation, and their motion is predictable in the same manner as that of the planets. Unpredictable, however, are the first appearances of "new" comets, i.e., those that have not been seen before. The reappearance of observed comets can be predicted if they are "periodic," that is, if their period of revolution is not too long, say, not over 100 to 200 years.

Big comets, of a size and brilliance likely to attract the attention of the man in the street, are rare; they appear only a few times in a century. But faint comets, visible only in telescopes, are observed quite often, several each year. The method of discovery and observation is at present mainly photographic.

Comets often reveal great fluctuations in brightness, which indicate that they cannot be steady and solid structures. As an example, we would mention comet Schaumasse; it is a typical case among many others.

Early in 1952, Comet Schaumasse (named for its discoverer) became visible in small telescopes, and in February, to the surprise of the observers, it reached the fifth magnitude, thus becoming accessible to binoculars and even faintly to the naked eye. It moved in the region of the Bowl of the Great Dipper, and had been known for 40 years as a relatively faint periodic comet, revolving around the sun in 8 years. During the 40 years it had approached the earth several times; observers had obtained accurate observations, and computers had calculated and predicted its path. In the autumn of 1951 the comet was found again close to the predicted position; but its luster became unusual at the beginning of 1952 when it flared up to 50 to 100 times the expected brightness. Something of an almost catastrophic nature must have happened to it. Considerable amounts of a volatile substance seem to have been exposed to the sunrays; vapors were formed which, by reflecting sunlight, rendered the comet many times more brilliant than before.

A comet is believed to consist of "ices" mixed with meteoric dust and stones. The "ices" are supposed to be ordinary frozen-water ice and various other substances which at terrestrial temperatures are in a gaseous state (e.g., carbonic acid gas), but have solidified in the extremely cold interplanetary space, at a great distance from the sun. When the comet enters the inner portions of the solar system, solar heat vaporizes the ices, which boil into the vacuum of interplanetary space. The vapors, or gases, liberated in such a way constitute the head and tail of the comet; the gases occupy a large volume and, being illuminated by the sun, become visible.

The amount of matter in the tail of a comet is very small and is in no proportion to its apparent size; therefore comet tails have sometimes been called "visible nothing." The comet itself, or the "icy mixture," is not conspicuous and looks like a pinpoint even in a telescope; this pinpoint constitutes the "nucleus" of the comet and contains most of its mass. The nucleus, although inconspicuous and often invisible, could be millions of times heavier than the gases which constitute the visible head and tail. But even the nucleus is rather unimportant by astronomical standards; it would take billions of the largest cometary nuclei to build up one earth. Most of them are less than one mile in diameter, very few as much as ten miles.

Under the action of sunrays the nucleus gradually shrinks; the "ices" vaporize (they never melt), some stones and dust are set free and become meteors, or shooting stars. The shrinkage of the nucleus and the vaporization of the "ices" may proceed unevenly; sometimes rifts are formed and the nucleus may break up into pieces. Normally, the surface of the nucleus will be covered with a layer of meteoric material which protects the inside from a too intense action of solar heat, but when a piece of the nucleus is broken off, or the protecting skin of meteoric material collapses, the ices will be exposed directly to the solar heat and will boil up like a drop of water on hot iron. Such an event would explain the sudden flare-up of a comet's brightness, as that described above.

Periodic comets are moving within the inner regions of the solar system, continually subject to intense solar radiation. Solar heat causes the vaporization of their substance; as a consequence the comet shrinks, even breaks into pieces. Fragmentation has been observed several times, when a comet breaks up into two or more independent comets. As a final outcome of fragmentation and vaporization, the comet will disappear. It can be estimated that, with the calculated rate of vaporization, periodic comets would last only for a few thousand years. Why, then, are many periodic comets still visible? Why have they not disappeared during the millions of centuries of the solar system's existence? The answer is that all periodic comets of old have indeed disappeared, and those visible now will disappear within a few thousand years. They will dissolve into gas, dust, and meteoric stones. The gas spreads all over the solar system, becoming invisible, or even leaves the system altogether, but the dust and stones continue to move on their orbits: they are then called meteors. When they enter the earth's atmosphere, meteors become visible for a fraction of a second; otherwise they are too small to be individually observable in interplanetary space. Yet space is filled with these remnants of decayed or decaying comets.

However, in place of those disintegrating, new comets enter our regions of the solar system. Most of the new comets are nonperiodic; they come from the outskirts of the solar system, from distances 1,000 times greater than that of Neptune, and normally return to these distances. Yet a few of them, when they approach the planets to a close range and overtake them from behind, are caught by the gravitational pull of the planets; their orbits are modified, made less elongated, and they become "periodic": they are prevented from returning to the depths of space. Instead, they begin moving within the inner regions of the solar system, where, of course, their fate is sealed, as was that of their predecessors.

The result of a close approach to a planet is not always capture. If the comet meets the planet from the front side, its motion being opposite to that of the planet, capture cannot take place; instead, the comet may be ejected from the solar system, its orbit being transformed into a hyperbolic one.

It follows that the depleting ranges of the periodic comets are being continually replenished by new captures; this explains why they are still there. The recruiting of fresh periodic comets, to replace those disintegrating, is chiefly the work of Jupiter, the "policeman" of the solar system: of all the planets, Jupiter plays the biggest part in the transformation of the elongated orbits of some newcomers into small periodic ellipses, as well as in the ejection of others from the solar system.

Only a few new nonperiodic comets appear each year. These normally return to the depths of space whence they came; Jupiter occasionally succeeds in catching one, converting it into a periodic comet.

The nonperiodic comets arrive from the outer regions of the solar system, from distances of 10,000 to 100,000 *astronomical units* (one astronomical unit equals 93 million miles, the distance of earth from sun). There on the outskirts of the solar system, but still within the reach and under the rule of solar gravitation, is a vast sphere occupied by the comets. The volume of this sphere is 10,000 million times greater than the volume of that portion of the solar system occupied by the known planets. Thus, inside the sphere of comets the region of planets is not more than a little village as compared with the entire surface of our globe. In this enormous volume there are believed to be about 100,000 million comets—little dark icy bodies, frozen to a temperature of −270°C. The temperature is so low because little radiation reaches these distant regions; there the sun looks just like another bright star, and more radiation comes from other stars than from the sun.

Most of these bodies move in large orbits which never come any nearer the sun. They may have remained in the distant cold regions of space since the beginning— since the formation of the solar system out of a nebula. The comets are perhaps remnants of this nebula, of the original material of which the solar system was built. It is also possible that they are fragments ejected in the beginning from the inner portions of the solar system by the action of planets. Although so numerous, they completely vanish in the emptiness of surrounding space: the average distance between two nuclei in the sphere of comets is about equal to the distance of Neptune from us! Also, their total mass, about equal to that of the earth, is not only negligible as compared with the mass of the solar system, but small as compared with that of the planets alone.

The comets in these outer regions are not only subject to the gravitational pull of the sun; other stars passing by may influence them as well. These *stellar perturbations* would change the orbits of the comets. However, stellar perturbations are important only in the outer regions because the attraction of the sun is weak there. In the inner regions of the solar system the influence of other stars is negligible and the sun reigns supreme.

As a result of stellar perturbations upon the sphere of comets, some of the objects—the cometary nuclei, without coma or tail—leave the solar system forever and enter interstellar space. Others have their orbits changed in such a manner that they fall toward the sun. Of course, the chances of actually hitting the sun in such a case are rather remote; instead, the nucleus will head for the inner portions of the solar system and, after there developing a head and tail, may become observable from earth as a "new," nonperiodic comet. Unless captured by Jupiter or another planet, it will return to the sphere of comets, the whole episode of plunging into our sunlit regions taking perhaps hundreds of thousands, or even millions, of years. There is little likelihood of the same comet's return; further stellar perturbations would utterly change its orbit, so that it would not come to the inner regions of the solar system. Thus, these "new" comets are truly nonperiodic, and truly "new" when they come within reach of terrestrial telescopes.

20. Meteors

METEORS ARE THE RUBBLE AND DUST OF THE UNIVERSE. The reader may ask: What is the use of studying these apparently unimportant bodies?

In science the importance of a body is not measured by its size, but by the role it, or its like, plays in nature. Great numbers may compensate for small size. The atom is the smallest of known bodies—yet the most important of all; the whole universe consists of atoms. From the technical standpoint, the atom has become a source of immense power and immense danger to mankind.

Meteors cannot boast of an importance equal to that of atoms. At present but a small fraction of the mass of the universe is in the form of small fragments. In the inner portions of the solar system the mass of meteoric matter is less than one thousand-millionth of that of the planets —an utterly negligible amount. In interstellar space in the Galaxy, or the Milky Way, dust is relatively more important; yet it accounts for only one part in ten thousand of the total mass of this stellar system. In spite of such a small relative mass, dust apparently plays the principal role in the formation of stars in the Galaxy. The nucleus around which a new star is born (and this still happens in our time) is created by meteoric dust; this, by its gravitational action, subsequently attracts gas and more dust from surrounding space. Thus, dust is the seed from which suns and planets have grown and are still growing.

Although the present share of meteoric matter in the solar system is negligible, this has not always been so. Thus 4,500 million years ago, in the solar nebula, when the sun and planets did not yet exist, about one per cent of the mass may have been meteoric dust, with 99 per cent gas. The dust condensed into nuclei of increasing size and so laid the foundation for the sun, planets, and comets. Those minute meteoric particles we are now observing are the very remnants of the material from which the earth and the other bodies of the solar system were built. This material is probably identical with that from which stars—other suns—have sprung.

Meteors, or shooting stars, are a common experience to anyone who watches the night sky for some time. The impression is that a star suddenly detaches itself and rolls down the firmament; at least, in such a manner shooting stars are described by popular tradition. Actually, the fixed stars—those distant suns, hundreds of light years away—have nothing to do with a shooting star. The latter—a meteor—is a little stony body, weighing not more than a grain of sand or gravel, which moves in space as an independent little planet. In space the meteor could not be seen because no telescope would reveal so minute a body at planetary distances. What we observed as a shooting star was actually the end of this body; it entered the terrestrial atmosphere with a cosmic velocity of some 10 to 40 miles a second and was instantly converted into vapor by the heat of friction. The vapors, in collision with air, emitted light and thus rendered the meteor visible for a fraction of a second; it shone while dying, a swan song in light and color. This happens not somewhere in distant space, but quite near to us, in the upper layers of our atmosphere at an altitude of perhaps 50 to 70 miles above the earth's surface.

Some meteors appear in "showers," coming from the same direction and moving parallel in space; a shower is active for only a few days, sometimes only a few hours, on specific dates of the year when the earth plunges into, and passes through, the meteor stream. Some showers yield 20 to 100 meteors per hour, others less; the less abundant showers can be traced only by assiduous observations. In exceptional cases there have been displays of several thousand meteors an hour, such as the Leonids in November of 1799, 1833, and 1866, or the Giacobinids of October 9, 1933. Many showers are connected with periodic comets, as is shown by their similar or common orbits; they represent, evidently, fragments detached from the comets. Other showers are not known to be associated with observed comets; these may be remnants of old periodic comets which have already disintegrated.

Most meteors, however, do not belong to showers; they move each in its own direction and, although small in numbers (from 3 to 10 per hour), are seen all the year round. These meteors are called *sporadic*. In spite of being less conspicuous than shower meteors on certain nights, the total number of sporadic meteors observable annually is four times that of shower meteors. Some of the sporadic meteors may be remnants of ancient showers dispersed by the perturbations of the planets. On the other hand, a very great proportion of them are moving in orbits of small eccentricity in the same direction as the earth; their motion resembles that of the planets, and they may not be of cometary origin. Possibly they are direct remnants of primordial matter, gradually spiraling into the sun from the asteroidal region; the force which makes them spiral and approach the sun is solar radiation, which acts as a resisting medium. Radiation possesses mass and weight, and is able to resist the motion of bodies. The obstacle offered to motion by solar radiation is, of course, very gentle; by terrestrial standards we would not notice it, but small bodies, say those less than an inch in diameter, when exposed in space to solar radiation for millions of years, will yield to this resistance. Their orbits will shrink in size and they will gradually approach the sun until they are swallowed by it. Thus, there is a continuous stream, a cloud of small particles, flowing into the sun in such a manner. The origin of these particles is outside the orbit of the earth; the larger particles would come from the asteroidal region, the finest dust—perhaps from the outskirts of the solar system.

Other sporadic meteors may belong to interstellar space. These would remain only temporarily in the solar system, leaving it again after a single passage. The presence of meteoric dust in interstellar space is made obvious by dark clouds which are seen against the background of the Milky Way; these clouds contain the finest dust, or smoke, which causes the absorption and is the reason for their dark appearance.

Although individual meteors are too small to be visible in interplanetary space, their combined light can be observed as the so-called *zodiacal light*. This is composed of a cloud of meteors, mostly very small (about one thousandth of an inch in diameter), gathered near the ecliptic (or the circle of the zodiac, whence the name). The zodiacal light can be observed in the spring after sunset, or in the autumn before sunrise, as a cone of faint light rising over the horizon from the sunset or sunrise directions. It can be seen easily by the naked eye in the countryside, unobstructed by city lights, early in the evening in spring, just when it gets dark. The particles chiefly responsible for this phenomenon are those spiraling into the sun under the action of solar radiation, as already described.

Whereas small meteors are completely vaporized in the upper atmosphere, larger bodies may lose only part of their substance from the surface, leaving a solid kernel which falls to the ground. Such "stones from heaven" are called *meteorites*. They may weigh from a few ounces to many tons. Meteorites are the only celestial bodies which we can lay our hands on and study by laboratory methods.

It was formerly believed that meteorites and ordinary meteors differ only in size. However, from the study of the behavior of meteors during their flight in the atmosphere it has become evident that there exist two different classes of object.

The small meteors, e.g., the majority of those visible to the naked eye, are fluffy or spongelike clusters of dust, such as would obtain by condensation from a gaseous state. They resemble snowflakes, except that these flakes consist of stone or iron dust. They may originate partly from the surface of comets, as explained in the previous chapter, partly from the direct condensation of primordial matter; in the latter case the flakes may represent the very substance from which the larger bodies were built.

On the other hand, the larger meteors (say, those exceeding half an inch in diameter) and the meteorites are dense stony or iron bodies which apparently have formed under high pressure, of the order of 50,000 atmospheres. This could have taken place only in the interior of small planets of the order of 600 to 1,200 miles in diameter. Two such planets may have been destroyed in a mutual collision, and their fragments now are traveling in space as meteorites and, perhaps, asteroids.

21. The Perseids: A Typical Meteor Shower

THE PERSEID METEOR SHOWER, CALLED ALSO "THE TEARS of Saint Lawrence," is the most persistent and, therefore, perhaps the best known of its kind. Records of it have been traced back to at least the ninth century of our era. While many showers reveal great fluctuations in their display, showing up brilliantly in certain years and at other times disappearing almost completely, the Perseids are known to lead regularly to a moderately conspicuous display year after year, with a frequency of 50 to 60 per hour on the day of maximum (August 11), and with an hourly rate of 10 to 20 on the days just before and after the maximum. The shooting stars of which the shower consists are little stony "skeletons" or "dust-balls," stoneflakes weighing 10 to 100 milligrams (0.1 to 1 grain); they may be from ⅛ to ½ inch in diameter. They enter the earth's atmosphere with a velocity of 35 miles per second and are vaporized within three to five tenths of a second, after covering a luminous track of 10 to 17 miles. They move around the sun in an elliptic orbit; the orbit is very elongated, its farther end reaching well beyond the orbits of Neptune and Pluto. It takes over a century for the particles to accomplish one revolution. Actually, they occupy a whole bunch or stream of orbits, some of which happen to intersect the orbit of the earth; only those particles moving on the intersecting orbits may collide with the earth and enter its atmosphere.

The stream of orbits of the Perseid meteors also contains the orbit of a comet—the third comet of the year 1862. The meteors are apparently "spray" or dust, detached from this parent comet and distributed all over the stream of orbits. Their orbits have been changed by the action of the planets, radiation pressure, and other factors.

The next appearance of the comet of the Perseid shower is expected around the year 1982. The comet's orbit, however, is such that it does not intersect the path of the earth; it passes our orbit at a distance of two million miles and, therefore, at present a collision with this comet is not possible. However, its orbit, like that of any other comet, is gradually changing on account of perturbations by the planets. Therefore, at certain times the orbit of this comet may temporarily happen to intersect the orbit of the earth; a collision then becomes possible (although not inevitable). Traces of such collisions are actually known on earth, in the form of *meteor craters*. About a score of such craters are known at present, in the United States, Canada, Australia, and elsewhere. They bear witness to catastrophic collisions with nuclei of comets, little planets, or giant meteorites, which happened in the not too remote past: say, within ten thousand to one million years before our time.

22. Collisions in Space

SPACE IS POPULATED BY BODIES OF GREAT VARIETY IN size, from the tiny dust particles or sand grains called meteors, to majestic suns, or "fixed" stars, hundreds of thousands of times bigger and heavier than our earth. These bodies move in all directions with enormous speeds, measuring 10 to 100 miles per second, or 30 to 300 times faster than an artillery shell. What would happen if two such bodies collided?

The catastrophic effects of a collision depend on the *kinetic energy,* or the energy of motion, which increases with the square of velocity; double velocity means a fourfold, triple velocity a ninefold energy for the same mass. Celestial bodies move 1,000 times faster than a railway train, and the destructive force of a celestial collision must be some million times greater than in a railway catastrophe for the same amount of mass involved. At a velocity of 20 miles per second the kinetic energy carried by each pound of the material is 100 times greater than the energy contained in one pound of dynamite. Therefore, a collision of two bodies moving with cosmic velocity will be tantamount to a terrific explosion.

As mentioned in the previous chapter, the earth bears traces of such explosions—the so-called meteor craters. An example is the large meteor crater in Arizona. It is a circular depression, 4,000 feet in diameter and several hundred feet deep, surrounded by a wall of uplifted rock strata. Thousands of years ago—we do not know exactly when it happened—a little planet, a nickel-iron chunk some 300 feet across, struck the earth; it pierced the atmosphere with a velocity of about 10 miles per second and produced a giant explosion in the Arizona desert near Canyon Diablo. The planet (or was it a comet's nucleus?) was partly vaporized, partly broken into numberless fragments which have been found lying around on the surface of the desert; the pieces were picked up by explorers and there are now some preserved in almost every museum of natural history. It is remarkable that the Indians did not touch these iron fragments. Perhaps prehistoric man witnessed the catastrophe; local Indians consider the spot haunted, tradition telling of a fiery demon having descended from heaven; the Spanish name of the place, "Devil's Canyon," is rather suggestive in this respect. The explosion, equivalent to some 10,000 atom bombs, must have destroyed life within a circle of at least 50 miles radius. Only distant witnesses of the event could have survived.

Happily, such catastrophes are rare, and the bodies which hit the earth are usually small. The impact of a planet (or cometary nucleus) of over 30 miles in diameter would exterminate all higher land animals by the shock wave and subsequent flooding. The geologically established continuity of evolution of life on earth indicates that no such collision can have happened during the past 200 million years. A body of 500 miles in diameter would have smashed the whole rocky mantle of the earth, not only exterminating all life, but erasing the traces of previous sedimental stratification. Now, recent radioactive age determinations prove the existence of preserved sediments almost 3,000 million years old, which even seem to contain remains of primitive plant life; this rules out a major catastrophe during all this interval of time.

Undoubtedly the number of stray bodies in the solar system decreases with time, because they are gradually being intercepted by the major planets. Therefore, if collisions were rare in the past, their number in the future must be even smaller. From the past history of our planet, undisturbed by major collisions, we may therefore expect an even safer future for hundreds, or even thousands, of millions of years to come. Of course, it is only an expectation, not a certainty—being alive is always synonymous with taking risks.

Astronomical observations of recent years have revealed a group of celestial objects which are in danger of colliding with our planet. At present there are six known minor planets which cross the orbit of the earth: Apollo, Adonis, Hermes, Icarus, and two as yet unnamed. Their orbits do not intersect ours but, on account of perturbations caused by the attraction of other planets, they are changing with the course of time and intersection may repeatedly take place, with the possibility of a collision. It has been calculated that in about 200 million years such a planet has a fair chance of hitting the earth. There must be many more such little bodies which, because of their smallness, are difficult to discover and are not yet known. It can be estimated that once in two million years a planet of this group, of a diameter ranging from 1,000 feet to 2 miles, may fall on the earth. The Arizona crater may be the product of impact of a smaller member of this group, which is estimated to have been about 300 feet in diameter. There must be a great number of such smaller bodies which cannot be observed telescopically; this follows from the fact gained by experience that small bodies are generally more numerous than large ones: sand grains are more numerous than boulders, small meteors more numerous than meteorites, etc. Therefore, although we cannot observe minor planets of 300 feet in diameter, we can safely assume that their number is very much greater than that of the larger, known objects.

Of course, nuclei of comets may also hit the earth from time to time, producing craters. Nevertheless, collisions with such objects are extremely rare and cannot represent a serious danger to life, chiefly because the number of stray bodies in the neighborhood of the earth is very small.

Not in all parts of the solar system is space as clean as in our vicinity; there are regions where planetary traffic is much more dangerous. From the known laws of planetary motion the chances of a collision between two bodies can be calculated in much the same manner as that used by insurance companies to calculate the expectation of life for persons of a given age. The actual span of life of an individual may greatly differ from the expected value, but the average will be more or less correct; were it not so, insurance companies would all have gone bankrupt. The writer has calculated the expectation of life for various minor members of the solar system; the results were published in the *Proceedings of the Royal Irish Academy* in Dublin some years ago.

Disregarding the comets, the space around the two inner planets, Venus and Mercury, is as clean as that around the earth. A few stray planets of the Apollo-Adonis group are known to move there, but they are small, less than a mile in diameter, and have a relatively short expectation of life, from 50 to 200 million years "only"; for such intervals of time they are likely to persist without colliding with, and being swallowed by, one of the big "regular" planets (earth among them). This explains why the space is so clean: the earth and the solar system have existed for about 4,500 million years, or much longer than the life of the ephemeral little planets. There might have been billions of such bodies at the beginning, when the solar system was formed, but they have long since disappeared. Those few observed at present must be newcomers, sent by planetary "perturbations" to our surroundings from other regions of space a few hundred million years ago.

There are also a few short-period comets and meteor streams entering the inner regions of the solar system and moving inside the orbit of Jupiter, such as Encke's and Giacobini's comets. Their expectation of life is a little longer—200 to 300 million years—than that of the Apollo-Adonis planets.

Unlike our surroundings, the space between the orbits of Mars and Jupiter contains a great number of minor planets or asteroids, of which about two thousand ranging from 10 to 500 miles in diameter have been discovered; yet millions of bodies of smaller size must be present, too small to be observed. Their total mass is about one thousandth that of the earth, and if put together they would make a body of perhaps 1,000 miles in diameter (our moon is 2,160 miles). Most of the asteroids do not cross the orbits of the major planets and are safe from collisions in this respect. That explains, of course, why they are still there. It is believed that they have been produced in a collision of two planets whose paths intersected. The fragments produced in the first catastrophe collided again and continue to do so, their number steadily increasing with time.

23. Mars, the Stone-battered Planet

OUR SOLAR SYSTEM IS BUILT ACCORDING TO A REMARKably regular pattern. The major planets circle the sun, all in the same direction and almost in the same plane.

Their orbits are nearly circular, very little elongated, and spaced at ever-increasing distances so that they do not intersect and cause the bodies to collide. The mass of the sun is 700 times the mass of all the planets together; the sun, therefore, firmly rules their courses, the feeble mutual attractions of the planets being unable to deflect them permanently from their present orbits. The solar system is solidly and safely built; as astronomers would put it, it is *secularly stable*. For thousands of millions of years to come the planets will remain at their present distances from the sun, without any risk of collision with one another. As we have seen, there are some small stray bodies which do not "keep to the rule" and may collide with the earth or the other planets, but no major catastrophes can be caused by them.

However, there are regions of the solar system where collisions are favored more than in others. In the previous chapter we mentioned the asteroids, situated between the orbits of Mars and Jupiter, which are probably the remains of a major catastrophe; they continue to collide with one another. Most of the asteroids keep to their own space, but a certain not inconsiderable number are crossing the orbit of Mars. Of these, at present 22 are known with diameters of between 8 and 56 miles, and 16 of smaller size. These bodies are much greater and more numerous than the asteroids of the Apollo-Adonis group that cross the orbit of the earth. The smaller ones among them are very difficult to observe; undoubtedly most of them remain invisible even with the largest telescopes.

There must be millions of little bodies in the vicinity of Mars, which, in collision with that planet, could produce meteor craters of a mile or more in diameter, i.e., equal to, or bigger than, the Canyon Diablo crater. There may be about 1,000 times more little planets in the vicinity of Mars than near the earth, some of considerable size and capable of producing catastrophes of global dimensions. The surface of Mars must be continually battered by small and large celestial projectiles. "Continually" is here, of course, taken astronomically: an interval of 1,000 years would be considered "short."

It can be estimated that once in 100,000 to 1,000,000

years a body of about one mile in diameter may strike
the surface of Mars, producing a crater some 10 miles
wide and cracks in the planet's crust. This may have
some bearing on the origin of the so-called "canals" of
Mars. These canals, radially diverging from dark spots,
or *oases,* may mark the cracks, the points of impact or
craters being identified with the oases. The pattern is
quite similar to that of a windowpane struck by a stone
or a bullet. For some reason (ground water, or fertility
of soil?) vegetation may develop more readily along the
cracks, rendering them visible to the terrestrial observer.
It is highly probable that in the night sky of Mars a continuous display of meteors takes place, produced by the
small pebble- or sand-grain-size asteroidal fragments;
the nightly displays would be equal in intensity to those
which on the earth can be seen for only a few hours once
or twice per century, on the occasion of extraordinary
showers. On Mars, on an ordinary night, the number of
meteors visible per hour may run into thousands, as
compared with only a few on earth. There would be another difference: the great meteoric displays on earth,
like the Leonids and the Giacobinids, consist of small
fluffy cometary fragments unable to penetrate our atmosphere, but the meteors falling on Mars would consist of
small and large stones, meteoritic fragments, many of
which would penetrate its tenuous atmosphere and hit
the ground. The surface of this planet seems to be under
continuous bombardment from above, of such intensity
as to constitute a constant and not by any means negligible hazard to life—if there is life on Mars.

24. The Stars

TO A SUPERFICIAL OBSERVER THOSE PINPOINTED LITTLE
sources of light which adorn the night sky are just stars
—all alike. To a more attentive observer who followed
the appearance of the sky for successive nights, months
and years, it would soon become evident that there is a
conspicuous difference in behavior between star and star.
Most of them remain in the same apparent position with
respect to one another, forming *constellations*. These constellations have been familiar to mankind from time im-

memorial; they have scarcely changed their appearance in the course of historical time, and the traditional constellations pictured on the firmament by the imagination of the ancients are still *our* constellations, of the same shape and called by the same fancy names as thousands of years ago, such as Ursa Major (also known to us as the Plough), Cassiopeia, Orion, Taurus, the Pleiades. But, in contrast with these "fixed" stars, as they are commonly designated, there are a few "wandering" stars, or planets, which change their place continually, day after day, and so conspicuously that anybody can verify it by marking the positions of a planet with respect to nearby stars on a map for some interval of time. Following the course of a planet among stars is one of the easiest kinds of observation for a nonastronomer.

When the astronomer talks about stars, it is always the fixed stars he has in mind, never the planets or the moon. The sun, however, is a star too, and not a planet, although it appears not to be fixed.

The sun shows considerable motion, like the planets, but its motion is even more regular than theirs. This solar annual motion is the reflection of the orbital motion of the earth; the sun itself stands more or less fixed at the center of the solar system.

However, it is not this relative fixedness but the physical nature of the sun which compels us to regard it as a star, similar in structure and properties to the thousands of twinkling pinpoints of the night sky. These are all distant suns, incandescent balls of gas, each sending out enormous amounts of heat and light. The only difference between our sun and the stars is that we are relatively near to our sun, whereas these other suns are far away. The nearest star, Alpha Centauri in the Southern Hemisphere, is 270,000 times more distant than the sun, and most naked-eye stars are 50 to 100 times farther still. Because of the great distance they appear faint, although some of them may exceed the sun in luminosity by multiples of hundreds, and even thousands.

The great distances which separate us from the stars cannot be conveniently expressed in miles—figures of 14 to 17 digits would be needed for that purpose. The *astronomical unit,* or the distance of earth from sun, is also too small. A more suitable unit is the *light year* or the

distance which light travels in one year—covering 186,-
000 miles in each second. The nearest star, Alpha Centauri, is 4 light years away; Sirius, 8 light years; the
Great Dipper, about 70 light years; and the farthest stars
of the Milky Way from 10,000 to 100,000 light years.

Our sun is the center and master of the planetary system. It governs the motions of its tiny subjects by gravitation; its heat and light maintain life on the surface of
at least one planet, our earth. The moon shines by reflected sunlight, and the other planets are rendered visible to us by the same means.

Do these other, distant suns reign over planets of their
own? Undoubtedly, although we cannot see their planets
even with the most powerful telescopes. To see planets
of the size of Venus, Earth, or Jupiter near another star,
we should have to use a telescope of some five miles in
length and about half a mile in diameter. Even disregarding the practical impossibility of constructing such a
monster telescope, it would show us nothing if the observing were done from the surface of the earth, because
of the instability of our atmosphere (which causes "twinkling" of the stars). The giant telescope would have to be
placed on the moon or on a small planet devoid of an
atmosphere to obtain full advantage of its optical power.
Even then it would show us only pinpointed sources of
light, circling around their central star and about as
bright as the planets of the solar system appear to the
naked eye. The surface structure of these stellar planets
would still remain a mystery to us.

Although planets of other stars cannot be seen, our
present telescopes often reveal two or more suns circling
around each other. These systems are called *double* or
multiple stars. Imagine another sun being present in the
solar system, illuminating and warming us sometimes at
night and in winter, when the principal sun fails! However, as was pointed out in previous chapters, the presence of a second sun would be of doubtful advantage to
us. Our position in a double system would be unstable
and dangerous.

The presence of invisible companions of stars is sometimes revealed by their gravitational influence. A visible
star having an invisible companion would show orbital
motion around the common center of gravity of the sys-

tem; this motion can be found from exact photographic measurements. By such a method the presence of invisible companions to several bright nearby stars has been indicated. To be detectable they must have a mass not less than about 0.01 of the solar mass, or 10 times the mass of Jupiter. A body of this size would no longer be self-luminous; it would be dark and, as with Jupiter, the temperature of its surface would depend entirely upon the radiation of its sun. Thus, by all standards, it should be called a planet.

Stars are freely suspended in space; nothing prevents them from moving. Their mutual gravitational attraction causes them to move with respect to one another, or with respect to the center of their common system, the Milky Way. Why, then, are the stars called "fixed"?

The name is misleading, indeed. The stars are no more fixed in space than are the planets; they are all moving. The spectroscope reveals motions of approach and recession of the stars, their velocities mostly ranging from 10 to 20 miles per second; some move ten times as fast. Thus, stellar velocities are of the same order of magnitude as those of the planets.

On the other hand, the apparent displacements of the stars on the celestial sphere are very small. Their position among the constellations does not change appreciably, as far as can be judged by the naked eye. The reason for this is their great distance.

Nevertheless, precise astronomical instruments, especially those based on photographic methods, are already able to reveal stellar displacements over intervals of 10 to 50 years. These displacements are called *proper motions*. An average star visible to the naked eye and placed at a distance of 300 light years would have a proper motion of about four seconds of arc per century; this would take the star across the diameter of the moon in 50,000 years! Clearly, such minute displacements cannot be noticed by the naked eye. No wonder the constellations have not changed appreciably within 2,000 to 4,000 years, since they were first outlined by the ancients.

Some nearby stars may appear to move much faster; e.g., the Great Dipper would change its shape appreciably within 50,000 years, and the fastest star in the sky would cover the diameter of the moon in 180 years. In contrast, the moon itself moves over its own diameter in about one hour; hence, the apparent motion of even the fastest star is 1.5 million times slower than that of the moon. Therefore, for most practical purposes we can still refer to the stars as being "fixed" with respect to one another, as far as their apparent position on the celestial sphere is concerned.

25. Orion

ORION, THE MIGHTY HUNTER OF THE ANCIENTS, CHASING Taurus, the ferocious bull, over the heavenly spaces, is the most conspicuous constellation of the winter evenings. It is one of the most brilliant groupings of bright stars in the sky, attracting the attention of the casual observer by its outward appearance. Apart from its folklore and appearance, it represents a unique collection of remarkable objects of study for the astronomer, who can there investigate the properties of unusual stars and nebulae.

The first-magnitude red star on the top left of the constellation, Betelgeuze, is a supergiant which in luminosity is ten thousand times, in volume millions of times greater than the sun. What we observe of that star is apparently an extended gaseous envelope of very low density, thousands of times less dense than atmospheric air, surrounding a very hot and very dense core in which the energy of the star is generated. The processes by which this energy is obtained are not yet known. If, as in the sun, the "ordinary" atomic energy sources are at work, Betelgeuze could live on them for not more than 10 million years. If such is the case, this star must be very young as compared with our sun, which is at least 400 times that old. However, the possibility must not be overlooked that Betelgeuze, as well as other red giant and supergiant stars, is in possession of a more powerful source of energy. The central regions of these stars may represent the laboratories where matter is directly transformed into energy; this would give 100 times more per unit mass than the conversion of hydrogen into helium, and several thousand times more than the terrestrial uranium sources to be used in the peaceful application of atomic energy.

In the bottom right-hand corner of the constellation is Rigel, a white supergiant, much hotter and more luminous than Betelgeuze, but of smaller volume. Rigel exceeds our sun in luminosity by about 60,000 times and is one of the most luminous objects of the Milky Way system; this supergiant has as companions, in lieu of planets, a binary —two blue suns, each of which is perhaps 100 times more brilliant than our sun. What was said about the energy sources and age of Betelgeuze applies equally to Rigel.

In the middle of the constellation is the Belt of Orion— three second-magnitude blue stars in a line. These stars are very hot on the surface, and normally dense; their true luminosity is not much below that of Rigel. It is highly probable that they are not "superhot" or "superdense" at the center, but are drawing upon the ordinary source of atomic energy; therefore they cannot be older than 5 million years.

Below the left star of the Belt stretches the Sword of Orion, a group of less brilliant blue stars, embedded in nebulosity. This is the famous gaseous Orion nebula, which represents but a condensation in vast stretches of the dust clouds and gas covering the whole of Orion as well as the neighboring constellation of Taurus.

According to our present state of knowledge, the grouping in space of most of the stars of Orion is not accidental; they are embedded in the nebulous clouds, being physically connected with them. There is little doubt that the stars originated from the clouds by condensation not more than 5 to 10 million years ago. In Orion the creation of new stars is quite a recent event, and is probably continuing. That is the reason why, for the astonomer, this constellation is one of the most thrilling regions of celestial space.

The greatest wonder of Orion is an object which, though less conspicuous than its giant stars and nebulosities, is of quite extraordinary significance in explaining the cycle of birth and death of the stars. It is a luminous ring, slightly elliptical but regular in shape, surrounding most of the constellation like a giant halo. The Belt and Sword of Orion are inside it, whereas Rigel on the south and Bellatrix in the north are on the ring. The ring is invisible to the eye and barely visible on ordinary photographs, which explains why for a long time it escaped detection. On red-sensitive plates and with a suitable red filter it is a very conspicuous feature. The red color of the ring is due to hydrogen; it is caused by the radiation of the so-called "H-alpha" spectral line of hydrogen, which is also responsible for the deep-red color of solar prominences.

This hydrogen ring is, of course, not a true ring. It is the edge of an almost spherical, thin shell of gas, like the skin of a balloon. The central portions of the shell are too thin to be visible, and it is only near the edge that the grazing line of sight encounters a sufficient thickness of the gas to make an impression on the photographic plate. The diameter of this hydrogen balloon in Orion is about 300 light years.

There are a few other similar hydrogen shells, or rings, within the Milky Way. One is known in the Large Magellanic Cloud, a "nearby" galaxy 150,000 light years away. The shells are 150 to 300 light years in diameter; that in the Large Megellanic Cloud contains a number of supergiant stars, forming a constellation whose absolute dimensions are nearly equal to those of Orion.

The most plausible explanation of such hydrogen shells consists in ascribing them to supernova explosions. A giant star at the end of its life, when the hydrogen fuel is used up in its central regions, is believed to become unstable. The outer regions of the star, containing plenty of unused hydrogen, are suddenly ignited and an explosion results: the whole star blows up like a hydrogen bomb. The products of the explosion, containing the major portion of the stellar mass, are blown out into space in all directions with a velocity of the order of 1,000 miles per second. An expanding cloud of gas, or a nebula, results.

It might be well to remind the reader that stellar explosions, although they involve enormous energies and high velocities, are rather slow phenomena by human standards. Heavenly spaces are so vast that these phenomena, instead of occupying a fraction of a second as on earth, will take long intervals of time, to be measured in years, or even thousands and millions of years.

In the year A.D. 1054 a supernova flared up in the

constellation of Taurus; on a spot where no star was previously seen, a star of unusual brightness suddenly became visible, and soon faded out gradually. This meant that a giant star of perhaps 15 times the solar mass ended in an explosion. At present, 900 years after the explosion, a gaseous nebula of 7 light years in diameter is seen in the place of the supernova. This is the Crab Nebula, still expanding at the rate of 800 miles per second.

Were there no obstacles in space, the debris of the explosion would dissipate with undiminished velocity and ultimately disappear. However, the space between the stars in our galaxy is not empty. It contains thinly dispersed hydrogen gas, to which other substances and some dust are admixed. This gas is pushed ahead of the expanding supernova nebula; it presents an obstacle which gradually slows down the expanding gases. An expanding gaseous shell is formed which, as it pushes outwards, sweeps together all the mass of interstellar gas encountered on its way: the velocity of expansion is so great that interstellar gas has no time to escape and is forcibly carried outwards. In such a manner the shell, as it advances, increases in mass, its velocity of expansion decreasing at the same time. This process will come to an end only when the velocity of expansion drops to about 1 to 2 miles per second, which is the velocity of the molecules of interstellar gas: only then will the interstellar gas be able to evade the advancing shell and escape. The average density of gas in interstellar space being known, it can be calculated that the Crab Nebula will attain a diameter of 70 light years 23,000 years from now; 140 light years in 260,000 years; 210 light years in 1.3 million years; and 280 light years in 4 million years, which is the maximum attainable diameter. After that the expanding shell will begin to dissipate. Curiously enough, these calculated future sizes of the shell into which the Crab Nebula will develop closely correspond to the observed diameters of the Orion Halo and other hydrogen rings. This agreement can be taken as a confirmation of the hypothesis of the origin of the rings from supernova explosions.

Judging by its size, the Orion Halo is near the end of its expansion. Its age is estimated to be from one to 10 million years, according to the mass of the original supernova. Perhaps 5 million years ago a star exploded some-where around the present center of the Halo—in the mid-dle of the constellation, near the star Eta Orionis and west of the Belt. The explosion swept up and compressed into an expanding shell a mass of interstellar gas of the order of 15,000 solar masses, 1,000 times greater than the original mass of the supernova.

Compressed gas and dust are believed to offer favor-able conditions for the condensation of diffuse matter into stars. Thus, the expanding shell of a supernova is a place where, if anywhere in space, new stars may be born. The material from which the new stars originate is mainly compressed interstellar gas; its mass is so very much greater than that of the exploded star that many new stars can be created. Of course, not all the compressed gas goes into stars; most of it may dissipate again into space. But, even allowing for this kind of loss, the super-nova death of a supergiant may lead to the birth of sev-eral new supergiants (like the three stars of the Belt, or Rigel), and of hundreds of smaller stars like our sun. In such a manner, supernova explosions can be compared to a process of seeding; in replacement of one star that perishes, many more new stars come into being.

Thus, whereas the extreme luminosities of the super-giant stars of Orion tell us that they must have been born recently, the Ring or Halo of Orion gives us a hint of how and when this could have happened. Some 5 million years ago a supergiant star, like Rigel or Betelgeuze, arrived at the stage of instability and exploded, creating an ex-panding shell of gas which by now has acquired the shape of the Orion Halo. On its way the shell produced several supergiant stars which now form the outline of the con-stellation, and many smaller stars which are less con-spicuous and can be observed only telescopically. The creation of new stars is probably still going on in the Orion Halo as well as in the wisps of gas and dust left behind, inside the expanding shell or "balloon," such as appears to be the case with the great nebula of Orion.

This does not imply that supernova explosions are the only means of making new stars. Clearly, the first super-nova must have originated in a different manner. Also, compression of interstellar gas can be brought about by collisions of gas clouds in space, or by pressure exerted by a heated portion of the gas upon the cold neighboring gas. There are indications that new stars are also born under these other conditions of compression.

With the "seeding" property of supernova explosions one could expect that all the interstellar gas would be rather quickly converted into stars, the process working at an accelerated rate as in the multiplication of living beings. However, as with living beings, there are factors working in the opposite direction. Stars are not only collecting matter from surrounding space, but are losing it back to space by a process similar to evaporation. Unimportant with small stars, this "evaporation" is considerable in supergiants; these, when the condensed gas from which they originated has dispersed, will begin "losing weight" and may not live to reach the stage when an explosion becomes possible. Similarly, they may break up into smaller stars before exploding. Thus, although in Orion ten supergiants may have been created since the original explosion, perhaps only one or two of them will reach the supernova stage and continue the chain of reproduction, the others ending their career in a different manner. Therefore, the multiplication of stars may not proceed very fast. Also, the matter collected into new stars may be balanced by the amount evaporated from all stars existing, old and new, and the quantity of interstellar gas may remain unaltered, just like the amount of oxygen in the terrestrial atmosphere. The mere presence of interstellar gas makes it quite probable that its losses and gains are, indeed, in equilibrium. This would mean a cycle like that of precipitation and evaporation of water on earth. In Orion we see the "clouds" (the nebulae) and the brilliant "raindrops" (newborn stars) which emerged from a cosmic "rainstorm," of which the Halo is the last remnant.

26. Stellar Systems

WHEN ONE SCANS THE SKY WITH A TELESCOPE AT HIGH magnifying power, among the myriads of randomly distributed stars one would note a few conspicuously close pairs. Such pairs of relatively bright stars, although of rare occurrence, are much more numerous than could be expected merely from accidental proximity, or perspective; the majority of them are, therefore, to be considered true physical systems in which the components are bound to each other by gravitation. Careful observations of orbital motion in the nearer stellar systems have proved, indeed, that the force which holds them together is the same as that which attaches the moon to the earth, and the planets to the sun. These systems are called double stars, or binaries; the term includes also triple and multiple stars, where more than two self-luminous suns have joined to form one gravitating system.

A brilliant example of a double star, already visible in a small telescope, is Mizar, or Zeta Ursae Majoris, the middle star in the tail of the Great Bear, or the handle of the Great Dipper. The two components of Mizar, of second and fourth magnitude, are visible at 50-fold magnification. They have a *common proper motion*, i.e., they move in the same direction with the same apparent speed of 13 seconds of arc per century; they cannot become separated and, therefore, they form one gravitational system. The distance between the components is more than 350 times the distance of earth from sun; their time of revolution around a common center of gravity may be about 2,000 years. Exact observations of double stars, and of this pair in particular, date only from 150 years ago; this is too short an interval to determine the shape of the orbit and period of revolution. Nevertheless, the relative orbital motion, ruled by the mutual attraction of the components, is clearly shown by the observations.

Only a few double stars—about 200 out of over 20,000 entered in double-star catalogues—show orbital motion that is fast enough for the determination of their orbits. Most double stars are so far away, and separated by such great distances, that no relative motion could be detected in a century of observation. The binaries are in a minority among the stars, which seem mostly to be single; not more than 10 per cent of all stars appear to be double.

The appearance, however, is deceptive. There must be a great many double or multiple stars whose components are too close together to be separately visible in a telescope. By considering the limitations of our telescopes, and the number of discovered double stars, it is possible to estimate the true number of double stars in the sky, allowing for those which remain invisible; the surprising conclusion is that most stars are double, triple, or multiple, each having on the average three self-luminous companions. Single stars, like our sun, are less frequent, numbering perhaps from 5 to 10 per cent of the total. However, because of the great distances, the binary or multiple nature of most stars cannot be observed directly. Only in some favorable cases can special methods of research disclose details of these invisible systems.

The spectroscope is a powerful means of discovering close double stars which cannot be separated in a telescope. While revolving around their common center of gravity, the components of a double star would alternately approach and recede from the terrestrial observer. This alternating motion reveals itself in the Doppler shift of spectral lines, which can be exactly measured. These systems, discovered by the spectroscopic method, are called *spectroscopic binaries*. In such a manner it has been found that each of the components of Mizar is itself a spectroscopic binary; so that, although it appears double in a telescope, it is actually a quadruple system. There are four suns, revolving in pairs around each other; the brightest of these is 20 times more luminous than our sun and the distance of the system from us is 90 light years.

In some cases the binary character of a star is revealed by its variation of light: when the orbital plane of the binary happens to pass close to the line of sight, the components may from time to time eclipse each other. During such a stellar eclipse the apparent brightness of the star decreases. The second brightest star in Perseus, Algol, is an example of such an eclipsing binary star.

One of the most conspicuous objects of winter evenings is the bright star Capella, or Alpha Aurigae. It becomes visible soon after dusk in the east-northeastern sky in November and moves gradually higher as the season advances, until it is near the zenith at dusk in February. It is one of the brightest stars in the sky. Except for its brightness, it shows nothing peculiar to the eye or to the most powerful telescope—it is just an intensely luminous dot. The spectroscope, however, reveals that Capella is a double star, a system of two suns revolving around each other just as the planets go around the sun. The components are *normal giants,* about 100 times more luminous than our sun. The appearance of this bright star is deceptive; it looks single, but actually it is a system of at least two large bodies, perhaps with many smaller ones in their company.

Such is probably the case with many of the fixed stars in the sky. Here is another example. About 5° southwest of Capella there is a pair of inconspicuous stars, less than a degree apart and well visible to the naked eye. The fainter of the two, that on the right-hand side, is Zeta Aurigae, a fourth-magnitude star which has turned out to be one of the most remarkable stellar systems—a spectroscopic and an eclipsing binary at the same time. There are two suns. The larger one is a giant of 22 times the solar mass and 205 times the solar diameter, emitting 4,800 times more radiant heat than our sun does. Its dimensions are almost equal to those of the orbit of the earth, and its radiation from the distance of 93 million miles would heat up the surface of our globe to the temperature of molten iron. Its companion, 10 times heavier and 250 times more luminous than our sun, revolves around the principal star in somewhat less than three years. The principal star is red, the companion blue. The safe distance for a planet, from the standpoint of a temperature convenient for life, would be 70 times the present distance of earth, or more than double that of Neptune, from the sun. The time of revolution, or the "year," of such a planet would equal about one hundred of our years. How different living conditions would appear to us if one year covered more than a lifetime! However, these two giant suns are so luminous that they cannot have existed for more than 100 million years, which is the length of time their hydrogen fuel would last. From what we know about the development of life on earth, 100 million years would be too short an interval for living organisms to attain a diversity of form and a level of organization comparable to that on our planet. Giant suns are too short-lived to shelter advanced stages of organic life on their planets.

In an earlier chapter it was mentioned that in double (or multiple) systems the orbits of planets are unstable and, therefore, unsuitable for life. This refers to planets which come within the efficient sphere of action of both suns of the system. However, if the distance of the planet from the nearer sun, around which it revolves, is considerably smaller than the distance between the two suns, its position will be as that of our moon or of the satellites of Jupiter. Therefore, planets which remain relatively close to one member of a double or multiple system are quite safe, from the standpoint of stability of their orbits. For instance, the nearest star, Alpha Centauri, is a double sun, its components separated by a distance about equal to that of Uranus from us. A planet revolving around one component of this system at a distance of some 100 million miles would find itself in a quite safe position as far as the stability of its orbit was concerned. The principal component of Alpha Centauri is but slightly brighter than our sun; its imaginary planet, 100 million miles distant, would receive about the same amount of heat as the earth gets from the sun. Thus, life could well exist and develop in the system of Alpha Centauri, provided that there were planets of the right quality and in the right position. The same applies to other dwarf stellar systems in which the self-luminous components are of about solar luminosity, and are either farther apart than Jupiter and the sun or closer than one fifth of the distance of earth from sun. Life is not quite impossible in double or multiple systems; only, the required favorable conditions are less likely to be met there than in single systems.

27. The Milky Way

ON A CLEAR MOONLESS NIGHT IN AUGUST, AMONG THE numberless faint and bright stars strewn all over the darkness of the summer sky, a delicately luminescent band of light, without sharp outlines, stretches overhead, rising from the northeast and approaching the horizon due south. In the mythology of various peoples it was called the Galaxy; the Milky Way; the Way of the

Birds; the Way of the Spirits, by which the souls of the dead went to the upper world.

Many stars are seen on the Milky Way belt. The most conspicuous constellations on it, for observers in northern latitudes, are Cassiopeia, Cepheus, Cygnus, Aquila. Outside the belt, stars are also numerous, the brightest visible in August evenings being Vega, seen almost overhead; next to it in brightness are Altair, in Aquila, and Deneb, in Cygnus, both within the belt.

At another time of the year, or at other hours of the night, the position of the Milky Way with respect to the horizon is, of course, different; other portions of it may become visible. Thus, in winter evenings the Milky Way belt is seen stretching over Cassiopeia, Perseus, Auriga, Gemini, Orion, with even more bright stars like Capella, Betelgeuze, Rigel and Sirius on or near it. However, the belt itself is more conspicuous in summer-autumn, in the region of Cygnus-Aquila. The belt continues to the Southern Hemisphere, to portions invisible from our northern latitudes: from Sirius down to the Southern Cross, thence over Centaurus to Sagittarius, and back to the Northern Hemisphere in Aquila. The galactic belt is, thus, a complete ring, in the middle of which we appear to be placed.

The first impression of the Milky Way does not suggest any obvious relationship between it and the stars. Yet, already in the eighteenth century, Thomas Wright of Durham declared that the Milky Way consists of stars gathered into a flattened, lens-shaped system or cloud; the stars and the Milky Way are one and the same thing, looked at from different viewpoints. The Milky Way belt is but the result of perspective, like the evening mist on a meadow, which resembles a belt surrounding us, yet recedes and evades us when we try to catch it.

Just as single trees are seen at a close range, whereas the outlines of a forest can be discerned only from a distance, so are the nearer stars visible separately, whereas the farther ones—millions of them, each too far away and too faint to be seen individually—melt into the dim outline of the Milky Way cloud of which they form part. All those stars called "fixed," all those distant suns, belong to the Milky Way; our sun being one among them. We are inside, and part of, the Milky Way system, that is why we cannot see its true shape, but only a bright belt in the direction where its extent is greatest.

Large telescopes, equipped with photographic apparatus, confirm that the Milky Way consists of stars, thousands of which can be counted in an area not larger than the face of the full moon. Yet not all stars of the Milky Way can be observed; most of them are too faint for even the largest telescopes.

Nevertheless, the total number of stars in the Galaxy can be approximately estimated from the combined gravitational force which they exert on individual stars. Like our solar system, the Milky Way is held together by gravitation, and prevented from collapsing by the centrifugal force of rotation. With this difference, however: in the solar system there exists a central body, the sun, which is a thousand times more massive than all its subjects, the planets, together, and rules unchallenged, by virtue of its mass—a true dictatorship; on the contrary, in the Milky Way there is no central body, only a common center of gravity, an imaginary point around which the stars are revolving as equals—the model of a republic. Yet the laws of gravitation and centrifugal force are in both cases the same. From these laws it has been calculated that the total mass of the Milky Way equals about 200,000 million solar masses; this figure also represents, roughly, the total number of stars in the Galaxy, which, thus, contains about one hundred times more suns than the number of human beings populating the earth. The great majority of these suns revolve around the galactic center in approximately the same direction, remaining near the plane of the Milky Way. From the spot where our sun is situated, galactic rotation (which also carries along the sun and its planets) is directed toward Cygnus, with a speed of almost 150 miles a second; the radius of rotation, or the distance of the sun from the center, is 27,000 light years, which is 2,000 million times greater than the distance of earth from sun. The time required for one revolution around the galactic center is nearly 200 million years, and the over-all diameter of the Galaxy exceeds 100,000 light years.

The center itself is situated in Sagittarius, most of its surroundings being hidden from us by clouds of dust. On red-sensitive photographic plates, which for penetrating the dust veil are better than ordinary blue-sensitive ones, enormous gatherings of stars are observed in the direction of the center. Radio waves, which can penetrate dust clouds or ordinary water-vapor clouds almost unhindered, reveal an extraordinary concentration of matter near the center—the *galactic nucleus*. Thus, although a republic without a permanent ruler, the Galaxy has an administrative center, a metropolis— the nucleus—whose stellar population amounts to at least 1,000 million suns: one hundred times greater than the human population of London or New York.

Individual stars, in revolving around the galactic center, do not follow exactly circular orbits. Most of the stellar orbits are elongated, so that the distance of a star from the center varies in the course of time. The orbits, however, are not ellipses, as would obtain in a two-body system, but more complicated curves; they can be represented by ellipses whose major axes also rotate. In such a manner the orbit of a star is not closed; it is a rosette with loops that never repeat themselves; a star never returns to the same place in the Galaxy (you may be left to ponder the philosophical question: What is meant by the "same place"?). Actually, because of perturbations by other planets, and also because of General Relativity, the orbit of a planet in the solar system is also a kind of rosette, never a true ellipse; but the deviation from ellipticity is here very small and can be disregarded for most purposes, whereas in the stellar universe the deviations are large.

Galactic rotation is derived from the observation of the motions of very distant objects. Nearby stars would not show it, because they share with us the same rotational motion. What we observe as relative motion (proper motion and radial velocity) of a nearby star is due, not to galactic rotation, but to the deviation of its galactic orbit (or that of our sun) from a circular one. The relative motions of individual stars, caused by these deviations, are of the order of only about 10 per cent of the velocity of galactic rotation, thus small and unable to change the general picture. They can be compared to passengers on the deck of an ocean liner; the liner moves with great speed, yet the passengers do not pay attention to this motion, which they share in common; they notice only their own relative "proper motion" with respect to each other while roaming the deck.

Not all the matter of the Galaxy is condensed into stars. A considerable proportion of it fills the space between the stars as gas and dust. Irregularities in the apparent brightness of the Milky Way belt, such as a dark marking in Cepheus, the Great Rift in Aquila which seems to split the Milky Way into two separate bands, and the Coal Sack near the Southern Cross, are easily visible to the naked eye; they bear testimony to clouds of absorbing matter—dust clouds producing the visible effect of obscuration—accompanied by much greater but invisible amounts of gas, mainly hydrogen and helium. The gas clouds, invisible to the eye and undetectable on ordinary photographs, are observed spectroscopically and, as far as hydrogen is concerned, are especially prominent in radio waves. The radio telescope, the most modern addition to the astronomer's equipment, has proved of decisive importance in disclosing the presence of gas clouds and revealing the structure of the Galaxy itself.

It has been found that gas and dust in the Galaxy are arranged along spiral arms similar to the arms of other, distant galaxies (spiral extragalactic nebulae). The arms start near the nucleus and wind outwards on a spiral, in the direction opposite to rotation, i.e., trailing behind. Between the spiral arms there is very little diffuse matter, but along the arms, amid the gas and dust, are found stars of high luminosity (like those of Orion). These very luminous stars are short-lived, and must be comparatively young; new ones are being created continually by condensation out of the diffuse matter. However, most of the ordinary faint or moderately luminous stars of the Galaxy appear to be old—as old as the Galaxy itself, and the solar system, which has existed for 4,500 million years. These old stars are especially numerous around the galactic center.

28. Other Milky Ways

SINCE TIME IMMEMORIAL MAN HAS STRAINED MIND AND imagination to construct a geometrical and mechanical picture—a plan, or cosmological model—of the world. In this task he has been greatly handicapped by perspective, nearby objects appearing to have a greatness and importance that did not correspond to their actual size and significance in the universe. Therefore in the early cosmologies man himself and his cosmic domicile, the earth, were given exaggerated roles, out of all proportion to their actual material importance.

With the advance of human thought the true proportions in the universe gradually became known. For obvious reasons, our knowledge expanded from the nearer celestial bodies towards the farther ones. Depending upon the accuracy of observations, at any time there was a limit of distance beyond which observations and measurements did not go. This limit defined a sphere inside which the situation could be explored and satisfactorily described, at least approximately or in general outlines, even when the precise distances and dimensions of the celestial bodies within it were not known.

Outside this sphere everything was left to conjecture. It is instructive to note how similar the new scientist's attitude was to that of primitive man or the ancients, when it came to describing the properties of the universe outside the sphere of the known: the importance of the known nearby portion was always overestimated, as compared with the regions far beyond. This especially refers to the "majority" or rank and file of the scientists; in their conservative or "cautious" mood, they for some reason thought—and, apparently, still think—that the small and unimportant is more likely to occur than its opposite, and preferred to adorn the unexplored with these attributes of lesser significance.

Of course, at all epochs there were a few minds that, with greater foresight and power of logic, were able to anticipate future discoveries; but, despite the weight of their arguments, they rarely convinced their contemporaries. One had to wait for centuries before the progress in observational technique impressed the doubting Thomas. A famous example of a man far ahead of his time was Aristarchus of Samos, who, in the third century B.C., was able to form a correct opinion of the structure of the solar system and the relative importance of earth and sun in it. His theory was discarded, not for lack of proof, but because of the refusal of philosophers and scientists even to consider his arguments. Eighteen hundred years elapsed before his views were successfully revived by Copernicus. Undoubtedly, caution and skepticism belong to the fundamentals of science, and should be applied without mercy to theories which are products of fantasy unsupported by facts. Yet, alas, too often these scissors of human thought have been used to cut off the evidence itself, thus becoming the instrument of wishful thinking and prejudice, protecting old traditions against new facts.

The story of the extragalactic nebulae represents the most recent stage in the widening of our sphere of exploration; as such it also bears the marks of a long struggle against skepticism and prejudice, although in a much milder form than, for example, in the struggles for the recognition of the rotation of the earth and the heliocentric model of the solar system.

By the middle of the eighteenth century the structure and dimensions of the solar system were pretty well known. That the fixed stars were other distant suns was also generally realized, and the ingenious theory of Thomas Wright of Durham interpreted the Milky Way as being an immense flattened cluster of suns. To Wright this system was "The Universe." Although little attention was paid to them in his homeland, Wright's ideas were readily accepted on the Continent, whence they returned to England.

In Germany, Lambert and Kant, displaying remarkable foresight, did not stop at Wright's explanation of the Milky Way, but expressed the belief that numerous nebulae which the telescope revealed, chiefly in parts of the sky that were outside the Milky Way belt, were other Milky Ways, "island universes," appearing faint on account of their great distance. At that time there was no knowledge of the diversity of types of nebulae, and it was believed that all nebulae are generally of the same nature. Lambert and Kant assumed them to be composed of stars, too faint and distant to be seen individually. We know now that their interpretation was correct with respect to the great majority of nebulae, excepting the gaseous ones and the diffuse clouds of our Milky Way. Sir William Herschel at first accepted their views; but, when confronted with such objects as the Great Orion Nebula or the disk-shaped "planetary" nebulae which, he felt, were located inside our universe of stars, he not only rejected the idea of island universes, but also thought that nebulae are not composed of stars but of some luminous fluid. He thus discovered by intuition the gaseous nebulae to which the above-mentioned objects belong. Their gaseous nature was proved spectroscopically 80 years later by Huggins. Yet Herschel unjustly made a generalization, ascribing to all nebulae the properties of these gaseous nebulae, which, as we know now, are actually in a minority.

Curiously enough, the avoidance by nebulae of the belt of the Milky Way was considered by Herschel an indication of their connection with our stellar system, whereas, according to our present knowledge, it proves just the opposite: the nebulae, situated far in space outside the Milky Way, are obscured by its clouds of dark matter and, therefore, are not seen on its belt; it is a purely optical effect. However, the correct explanation was given only in the twentieth century. For over a century Herschel's ideas prevailed as a "majority" view and Thomas Wright's universe of stars was looked on as *the* universe. Only during the first quarter of our century was the Milky Way finally denied this unique position and reduced to the status of a mere galaxy among innumerable millions of others.

The changeover was made easier by the fact that the idea of the island universes was never abandoned completely. Many leading thinkers of the intermediate period favored it. Yet doubting Thomas was not easily convinced. The author of these notes remembers two eminent astronomers whom he tried in vain to persuade of the correctness of the island-universe theory. One was a Russian astronomer whom he met at Pulkovo Observatory in 1920; the other was at Mount Wilson, in 1931. These learned gentlemen were great experts in the measurement of stellar positions on photographic plates. By comparing old and new photographs, they were trying to measure proper motions in spiral nebulae, and believed they had found certain displacements in them which confirmed each other's results. Yet the results proved erroneous because of systematic differences between the nebular images on the old plates and those on the new; nebulous knots, unlike pointlike stars, showed spurious displacements depending upon the quality of the plates. This should have been obvious to those who accepted the island-universe theory and the enormous distances of the extragalactic nebulae. At these distances the measured displacements would have called for enormous velocities of rotation, approaching that of light; as well as being physically impossible, this was contradicted by spectroscopic observations, which gave velocities of rotation about 1,000 times smaller than the velocity of light.

The final proof of the extragalactic nature of the nebulae that convinced all disbelievers was given by Edwin P. Hubble at Mount Wilson Observatory. He succeeded in photographing and measuring the light of some individual giant stars in the nearest nebulae; similar stars, of a particular type of variable brightness (so-called *Cepheids*), were already known and studied in our Milky Way. The difference in apparent brightness between these stars in our neighborhood and those in the nebulae led to the calculation of the distances and true dimensions of the latter.

It turned out that most of the nebulae are extragalactic, or true island universes, composed of thousands of millions of suns intermingled with gas and dust. For some reason connected with the rotation of these objects, the diffuse matter—the gas and dust—assumes spiral forms, like a spoonful of milk dropped into a stirred-up cup of tea; nebulae containing diffuse matter assume a characteristic appearance which led to their designation as *spiral* nebulae. Others, being devoid of gas and dust, do not reveal a spiral structure and are called *elliptical* nebulae. It is now believed that the elliptical nebulae have lost their diffuse matter in encounters with other nebulae which brushed the gas away, leaving the stars intact.

The properties of the extragalactic nebulae are similar to those of our Galaxy, and most of what was said about the Milky Way refers also to them. They are "republics," each consisting of 1,000 to 100,000 million suns rotating around a common center of gravity, with a nucleus or denser star-cloud surrounding the center. The nearest of them are the two Magellanic Clouds, visible in the Southern Hemisphere; they are 150,000 light years away. The distance of the great nebula in Andromeda—a close replica of our Milky Way—is 1.5 million light years; from the most distant nebulae accessible to the largest telescopes, it takes light 1,000 million years to reach us.

There are thousands of millions of such nebulae. Although their number is great, it is believed that it is not infinite. According to Eddington, the total number of nebulae in the universe is about 100,000 million, or about as many as there are suns in one nebula. Hence the total number of suns in the universe is a figure of 23 digits—10,000 million million million. If the surface of the earth were taken to represent the universe, there would be 10,000 suns per square inch. The estimate of the number of suns may be incorrect, but, if so, it errs on the low side of the true number.

Each of these numberless suns is a potential center of a planetary system. Most of the planets are probably uninhabited, yet many may carry life on their surface. Even if there were only one inhabited system in every million, there would be 10,000 million million abodes of life in the universe. What a variety of forms and conditions this implies!

29. The Expanding Universe:
Its Origin and Fate

THE STUDY OF THE DISTANCES AND MOTIONS OF EXTRA-galactic nebulae represents one of the most spectacular chapters of astronomy in the twentieth century. It led, in the first place, to the understanding of the structure of these nebulae—these other Milky Ways, consisting of numberless millions of suns and their planets, potential carriers of life. Yet the consequences of the study are much more far-reaching than that: unexpectedly we have come close to the question of the origins of our world.

The observational fact which made possible an approach to this problem, considered insoluble until now, was provided by the astronomer's "magic eye"—the spectroscope. The spectra of the nebulae, consisting of a continuous color band from red to violet, interrupted by dark Fraunhofer lines of absorption similar to those observed in the sun and stars, indicated that the nebulae consisted, indeed, of stars or suns, as was anticipated 200 years ago by Lambert and Kant. The positions of the absorption lines, however, did not coincide exactly with those of the solar spectrum, but were found to be displaced systematically towards the red, and the greater the displacement, the fainter and more distant were the nebulae. This phenomenon is called the *red shift*. It would indicate that the nebulae are moving away from us; the farther they are, the faster they move.

Of course, the stars of our Milky Way also reveal shifts of their spectral lines. However, these shifts are taking place both ways, toward the red and blue ends of the spectrum, indicating motions of recession and approach, whereas the nebular shifts are one-sided, revealing only recession. Further, the velocities of the stars are relatively small, being of the order of those encountered within the solar system, from 10 to 200 kilometers per second, while nebular motions attain thousands of kilometers per second, the highest value so far recorded being 60,000 kilometers per second. For this reason the nebular red shifts are rightly considered to have a more profound significance than the random motions of the stars. They have become the chief clue to the interpretation of the structure and life history of the whole world, and not only of a limited part of it.

If science is not to be judged by technical achievements, but by its contribution to the understanding of the universe and our place in it, one of its greatest successes in modern times consists in this tackling of the problems of the beginning of our material world and its future fate. Not that final answers have been obtained, but the problems have been put on a concrete basis for the first time in the history of human thought; in particular, a picture of the evolution of the universe for the past 4,000 or 5,000 million years can now be drawn with little ambiguity.

The fundamental question is that of the beginning and age of the universe. By the end of the nineteenth century this problem still remained outside the realm of exact science, simply for lack of observational approach. Of course, the second law of thermodynamics was already established. This stated that thermal evolution is a one-way process, like the run of a clock which is not kept wound up; heat flows from hotter towards colder bodies and is lost by radiation to space; an equalization of the temperature of different parts of the universe follows. Given sufficient intervals of time, a state of equalization of temperature would result, that of Nernst's *Wärmetod* or thermal death, where, in the absence of temperature differences, no relative motion except that of molecules could take place. The state of our present world is certainly very remote from the lethargy of equalization. The mere fact that temperature differences exist, that suns shine and planets carry life on their surface, in defiance of the insatiable immensities of heat-absorbing space, would point to the youthfulness of the world. If so, there must have been a beginning; and, inevitably, there must also be an end.

Scientists of half a century ago somehow preferred to ignore this writing on the wall. One of the reasons—or, rather, pretexts—for such an attitude was that the speed with which the universe is approaching equalization is unknown and may be very slow; thus, the time intervals required by this process may be very long. Without proper logical justification, the indefiniteness of the problem led to a widespread feeling that the universe should have neither beginning nor end, a viewpoint which was more influenced by opposition to former mythological or religious ideas of creation than by impartial reasoning.

Since the second decade of this century a number of new observational facts became known which entirely changed the outlook; they concordantly pointed to a finite age of our universe, of the order of a few thousand million years. Of these, the most revolutionary consequences were brought about by the red shift in the spectra of extragalactic nebulae. Being interpreted as a Doppler effect of motion, it indicated a recession of the nebulae; they are all moving away from us, and from one another, with velocities that increase with distance.

The discovery brought home to us a type of organized motion which hitherto was not known among cosmic systems. Over the entire hierarchy of these systems, from atoms to galaxies, we find that generally a rotational motion keeps the individual members of a system in equilibrium against the centripetal forces of attraction. Thus, the electrons revolve in atoms on their tiny orbits of less than one hundred-millionth of a centimeter in diameter; the moon and other satellites revolve around their respective planets at distances of several hundred thousand kilometers; the earth and her sister planets revolve around the sun, keeping to distances of several hundred million kilometers; the stars of the Milky Way system, a typical galaxy, whose extent is 100 million times that of the solar system, revolve around a common center of gravity; among them the sun, one of 100,000-odd million suns of the system, performs one revolution in about 200 million years. With this last-mentioned motion, called galactic rotation, ends the sequence of rotational systems in our universe.

Next comes the system of extragalactic nebulae which already behaves in a different manner. The flattened shape of these other Milky Way systems indicates rotation within each of them, similar to galactic rotation, and this is also confirmed by direct spectroscopic observations of motion. They are separated from one another by gaps of almost empty space, measured in millions of light years, and the most distant ones still observable with the largest telescopes are over 1,000 million light years away—a million million times farther than the farthest known planets of the solar system.

In all directions of space where the view is not obstructed by local Milky Way clouds of cosmic smoke, extragalactic nebulae are visible more or less uniformly. There exist groupings or clusters of nebulae which, however, do not influence the general picture of uniformity. The uniformity of the distribution, without preference for a particular plane, distinguishes the universe of the nebulae from subordinate systems in which planes of preference are prominent. The peculiarity of motion—the recession of the nebulae—explains this peculiarity in distribution: there is no systematic rotational motion among them, only a radial motion of *expansion*. The nebulae are moving away not only from the terrestrial observer, but also from one another.

A belief has been formed that the universe of extragalactic nebulae is the last step in the hierarchy of cosmic systems, or that it embodies the universe itself; no further systems of a higher order are expected to exist. Although only a belief, it has proved a fruitful working hypothesis. The peculiar distribution of motions in this supersystem, as well as the high velocities of recession encountered—60,000 kilometers per second or one fifth of the velocity of light being the observed value for the remotest nebulae, without any sign that the increase of velocity with distance would stop at that value—points to its unique position.

Thus, we choose to say that the universe itself is expanding in all directions. The word "expansion," although scientifically precise, is too modest to convey to lay ears the meaning of what is actually happening. The observed velocities of recession correspond to energies per unit mass equal to seven times those released in the explosion of a hydrogen bomb. In the unobserved range the velocities are doubtless even greater. We are witnesses to an explosion involving the whole universe, of an intensity surpassing everything hitherto encountered on earth. The fragments of the explosion—the galaxies —are flying apart with velocities which exceed a hundred thousand times the velocities in the most violent non-atomic terrestrial explosion. In a corner of one of these fragments—the Milky Way—is our sun, sheltering the planet Earth where life is nestling, where the marvel of the human mind is prying into the mysteries of the cosmos. We have just discovered our precarious position, sitting like Baron Munchausen on a flying bombshell, and are wondering what is coming next. Whence have we come, and where will we land? Is there time enough for us to fulfill our destination?

As to time, there is even too much of it. The velocities of the cosmic projectiles are great, but so also are the distances to be covered. If the present velocities of recession of the nebulae remained unaltered, their distances would be doubled in 6,700 million years. Actually, restrained by gravitation, the velocities will decrease with time, and the time of expansion will be even greater than the above-mentioned figure. We can be sure that doubling of the nebular distances would not mean fundamental changes in the properties of our universe. It follows that there are many thousand million years ahead for the happenings inside the subordinate systems, in the suns and on the surfaces of their planets, to pursue their normal course without being influenced by the universal expansion. It took "only" 500 million years for life on earth to develop from the primitive forms of the early Cambrian to the present-day level and diversity of forms; man entered the stage less than a million years ago, and his civilization has lasted for less than 10,000 years. The time of doubling the nebular distances is one million times longer than the duration of our civilization, and exceeds twenty times the post-Cambrian span of organic evolution. There is plenty of time ahead. Our position on a fragment of a cosmic superexplosion is not so precarious, after all. As to the consequences of the explosion, we can feel at present perfectly safe and comfortable and make plans for the future, not only for our immediate descendants, but also for those creatures of a higher order which may succeed man after millions of centuries. This does not mean that there are no cosmic dangers in the future; for instance, our sun may play a bad trick on life on earth within the coming 1,000 million years by becoming so hot that the oceans will boil. However, this and other menaces are in no relation to the phenomenon of universal expansion, whose influence upon the fate of individual worlds will not come into play for, say, 25,000 million years, and then only if the present expansion stops, and is followed by a contraction.

So much for the future; but what about the past? Tracing the expansion back in time, we find that the universe was in a more compact state, the distances between the nebulae having been the smaller the farther into the past we go. The velocities of recession were greater than now, because since then gravitational attraction has been slowing them down; this means that the recession of the nebulae never stopped in the past, and that there was a moment when the nebulae were in contact. The contact must have taken place simultaneously for all nebulae, because their velocities of recession are proportional to their mutual distances, and the time required to cover any distance is the same for all. Modern astronomical data for the velocities of recession, the distances of the nebulae and the average amount of gravitating matter per unit volume in the universe, interpreted on the basis of the Friedmann–Einstein "cosmological model" (gravitation versus expansion), set the time of contact as 4,500 million years ago. This figure can be called the age of the universe in a restricted sense. Actually, it is the duration of the present stage of the universe, without prejudice to what was, or whether there was anything at all, before. When in contact, the whole matter of the universe must have been dissolved into a uniform substance; all the classes of celestial bodies which are familiar to us now must have been completely absent.

Thus, the universe exploded 4,500 million years ago from a superdense state: this was the beginning of our present universe. The elastic forces which sent the fragments flying with velocities of at least one fifth of that of light could not have originated anywhere but in the most condensed state of matter known to the physicist, the so-called *nuclear fluid*. This is the substance that fills the interior of atomic nuclei; one cubic centimeter of nuclear fluid weighs 250 million tons. At that density the whole universe—which is believed, rightly or not, to be of finite mass—would have been squeezed into a volume equal to that of a sphere of 220 million kilometers' radius, or about that of the orbit of Mars. Lemaître was the first to visualize such an initial state of the universe; he pointed out that, at the density of nuclear fluid, this state would correspond to one giant atom. This "primeval atom," "the egg from which the universe hatched," must have been unstable, in the same manner as are radioactively unstable all atoms heavier than bismuth. It must have decayed spontaneously, exploding the instant it was formed. Our present universe would thus consist of the debris of radioactive decay of one single atom!

How did the primeval atom come into being? If it had no predecessor, it must have been created on the spot. It would seem that here, in the absence of positive evidence, the acceptance of an Act of Creation could be left to the taste and esthetic judgment of those concerned with the problem.

The alternative would be contained in the assumption of a previous state, a *collapsing* universe which crashed from all directions into one spot. The collapse was stopped at the maximum possible density of matter, that of nuclear fluid, whose elastic forces not only broke the impact, but sent the universe back expanding, like a rubber ball rebounding from a wall. The primeval atom would in this case be deprived of its unique significance; it would represent only a transient stage of maximum compression.

The question arises: Where did the previous collapsing universe come from? To do away with the necessity of assuming the spontaneous creation of a collapsing universe, which would appear much less plausible than the creation of the primeval atom, we are compelled to assume its origin from an expanding universe whose expansion was somewhere stopped by gravitation and converted into contraction, or collapse. We arrive thus at the picture of an oscillating universe, the "cosmic pendulum," which expands to a certain maximum volume, then contracts and rebounds from the almost pointlike state of maximum density to start the next stage of expansion, and so forth.

Theoreticians have, of course, foreseen the possibility of an oscillating universe. Some observational data which are now available seem to give support to this model. An expanding universe may develop along two different lines, according to the actual amount of matter in it. If the amount of matter is below a certain limit, gravitation will be unable to halt expansion; the universe will continue expanding indefinitely and irreversibly. On the contrary, if there is more matter than the limit, gravitation will ultimately prevail—expansion will cease, to be succeeded by contraction; this is the case of the oscillating universe.

Whether or not the real universe is of the oscillating type depends thus upon the "world density," or the average amount of matter per unit volume of space. The limiting, or critical, value of world density, for the observed rate of recession of the nebulae, is 39 grams of matter within a cube of 100,000 kilometer edge (not very much, indeed); an estimate of the actual world density by the writer gave 25 grams, or 64 per cent of the critical value. The result could easily be in error by as much as a factor of 2, or even more. If this result is taken literally, it would mean that the universe is irreversibly expanding. However, the opposite conclusion appears to be warranted here. We note that a relatively small increase, by about 60 per cent of the estimated value, would bring it above the critical limit. The estimate, based upon the gravitational attraction which a cluster of galaxies (the Virgo cluster) exerts upon its members, takes into account only the mass of the cluster, neglecting the diffuse matter (gas, dust, and stray stars) which may be present in greater amounts in "open space" outside the cluster. Indeed, Zwicky at Mount Wilson has found indications of great amounts of diffuse matter in intergalactic space and arrives at a world density 25 times our value; although his estimate is based only upon the outer appearance of the patches of diffuse matter, and is therefore less reliable than ours, it definitely points to a higher value of the world density. Therefore, it is highly probable that the world density exceeds the critical value, although perhaps only slightly, and that the universe is of the oscillating type. Let us consider some consequences of this hypothesis.

The timetable of the "cosmic pendulum" could then be roughly as follows. The excess of world density over the critical value being slight, it would mean that the expansion is still in full swing, and that its climax is far ahead, perhaps 10,000 million years from now. With the 5,000-odd million years in the past, this gives 15,000 million years as the total duration of expansion, and an equal interval of time for the ensuing contraction. The total duration of a cycle of oscillation is thus of the order of 30,000 million years, or nearly seven times the age of the solar system or the duration of past expansion. During this interval of time, which could be called the "cosmic year" ("the Day of Brahma"), galaxies, stars and planets are formed, so to speak, in flight; suns are born and become extinct, or explode; life develops on the surface of planets, and perishes.

At present we are in the beginning of a cycle of cosmic oscillation. The "age of the universe," the 4,500 million years of past expansion, is not a true age but only the time elapsed since the last rebirth of the world, which took place in the state of greatest compression into which the universe had previously crashed. Our sun with its planetary system came into being soon after the start of the present expansion, and can now look back upon more than one half of its lifetime; from what we know about stellar structure and evolution, it will not last for more than a further 3,000 to 4,000 million years. Life may disappear from the surface of our planet long before that. There will be other suns, some newly born from interstellar clouds, some those fainter ones which do not spend their energy so profusely and therefore last longer; many of them will shelter life in corners of the innumerable galaxies of the universe, long after our sun has gone.

Some 25,000 million years from now the Day of Reckoning will come. The whole universe—all galaxies with their suns shining or extinct, their planets dead or still carrying life on their surface—will precipitate itself into a narrow space, almost a point. Everything will perish in a fiery chaos well before the point of greatest compression is reached. All bodies and all atoms of the world will dissolve into the nuclear fluid of the primeval atom—which in this case is not truly primeval—and a new expanding world will surge from it, like Phoenix out of the ashes, rejuvenated and full of creative vigor. No traces of the previous cycle will remain in the new world, which, free of traditions, will follow its course in producing galaxies, stars, living and thinking beings, guided only by its own laws—the laws of nature and God.

In each new oscillation, all the structural phases of the previous ones will repeat themselves, without, however, an "eternal recurrence of all things" in Nietzsche's sense. The exact repetition of individual phenomena will be practically impossible, being forbidden by the law of chance. Therefore, the individual celestial bodies in successive oscillations would not be identical, nor would their inhabitants. On the contrary, an unlimited variety of combinations and of prospects of evolution would be possible during each phase of the oscillation.

Disapproval, on purely esthetic grounds, of the idea of an oscillating universe repeating its general features has been voiced in some quarters; the prospect has been described as dull and uninviting. However, human esthetic considerations are here absolutely irrelevant. The only pertinent question is: What is the Plan of our world? We cannot insist upon the correctness or finality of our interpretation, which only claims a certain degree of probability. But, if the interpretation turns out to be correct, we have to accept it without demur, even though the Plan was laid down without our being consulted beforehand. Besides, we cannot see why the Great Repetition should claim a lesser esthetic value than, for example, the annual succession of seasons so praised by poet and layman. Would we call the coming spring dull because there has been springtime before? Or is today boring because sunrise and sunset have been recurring for eons in the past?

30. Life and Consciousness in the Universe

Know that the least of all the minds My will has made
Outweighs, not once, but many myriad times,
The mightiest mere mass: the thoughts of human hearts
Outvie the movements of a million suns,
The rush of systems infinite through space.
                                        —R. A. PROCTOR

LIKE THE ROMAN GOD JANUS, NATURE APPEARS TO US with two faces. One is the nonliving, inorganic world, ruled by physical laws among which *law of chance,* or the lack of coordination and obvious purpose, is the most prominent. The other is the organic world of living things, the biocosmos, where, in addition to the physical laws, strange coordinating or organizing factors are at work, and blind chance is eliminated to a great extent. If judged by mass, the inorganic world exceeds so immensely its living counterpart that the latter appears to be utterly insignificant; life can be compared to a fungus in some petty corners of the otherwise ideally clean universe.

Yet life is the carrier of the wonderful qualities of mind and consciousness, qualities which hint at the presence of a purpose in the universe. The overwhelming quantity of mass does not add to these qualities; its purpose appears to be the provision of a basis for life. In this respect nature is wasteful; through accidental combinations, only a small fraction of the material world happens to be suitable for the requirements of life.

The *material* world . . . The use of this word would imply the existence of its counterpart—an immaterial world. So-called materialists, whose name is legion among the rank and file of scientists, would object to the discrimination; they would contend that there is only one world, the material, and that everything, including mind or soul, follows from properties of matter, and is, therefore, material.

Such a standpoint is merely a playing with words. It amounts to calling two different things by one name (which may sometimes be a legitimate procedure) and then ascribing properties of one of them to the other, with no more justification for it than for the common name (which is, of course, illegitimate). Or, simply, it is a sophism.

The materialists contend that everything in the world is governed by physical laws, and that our inability to explain some phenomena on the basis of these laws is due only to imperfect knowledge. This is the so-called mechanistic viewpoint.

To clear up the situation, we ought to call a spade a spade. Material things are those which can be described quantitatively in terms of space and time. They are endowed with the properties of location and motion, contain measurable mass and energy (mass is only one form of energy; or, rather, mass is energy, and energy is mass), and have the power of influencing one another according to physical laws. The mechanistic concept would apply to material things defined in such a manner; a complete knowledge of the conditions in a material system would allow of a prediction of its fate. Yet even here, quantum mechanics has introduced a correction: the complete description, in terms of space and time, of a material system is impossible in *principle,* nor is it possible to make precise predictions for the evolution of a given initial state. Practically, however, this *uncertainty principle* applies only to microscopic events which proceed on an atomic scale; happenings on a

macroscopic scale in the large-scale material world surrounding us are reasonably predictable in the mechanistic sense. We note, however, that the uncertainty refers
here only to the *accuracy*; the *possibility* of expressing
material phenomena in terms of space and time, whether
precisely or not, is not questioned.

Immaterial things, on the contrary, cannot be represented in the framework of space and time; they cannot
be measured in physical units, nor do they obey physical
laws. The activities of the mind are one example of immaterial phenomena. Thought has neither dimensions
nor weight nor energy. Of course, the process of thinking may be connected with a physical effort, but it is not
the effort itself. Thinking may require a material brain,
but the outcome of it is immaterial. The thought
"$2 \times 2 = 4$" has no weight, its place and time being nowhere or everywhere; the concept of motion cannot be
applied to it. Two intellects—those of a giant and a
microscopic being—will arrive at the same conclusion,
although the physical efforts of their brains, measured in calories, may differ a billion times. Evidently,
the physical effort is only the framework of thought, not
thought itself.

A die-hard materialist would smile in his superior
manner and say: "*I* do not believe in this immaterial
stuff." Yet, by saying so, he proves the thing he denies.
What is this mysterious "I," the individual consciousness, in the name of which he is speaking? Has it dimensions? Weight? Age? Certainly not—these properties belong to the body with which consciousness is
connected, not to consciousness itself. Its only property
is that of existence; while it exists, it remains unchanged,
a thing outside space and time, eluding all attempts at
measurement. It is the only reality of which we have
immediate knowledge, the gate by which the cognition
of the rest of the world comes to us. Yet this sole reality
of which we are certain is immaterial. The immaterial
"I" of a materialist denying the existence of immaterial
things—can there be a greater paradox?

Thus, the only primary reality to us is our "I"; its
existence need not be proved—consciousness means existence itself; it comes even before mind and thought,
overriding the thesis of Descartes—"I think, therefore

I exist." What remains to be proved is the existence of an outside world. Thus, if there can be doubts, they would refer to the existence of material things.

Of course, our experience teaches us that, beyond reasonable doubt, the material world is a reality which behaves independently of our mind and fancy; yet this cannot overshadow the primary reality of the immaterial —of consciousness.

Experience with living beings, by way of analogy, leads us to the recognition of other consciousnesses. There is no direct proof in this respect; it is not possible to replace our consciousness by that of a fellow being, to compare them in the same manner as are compared the weights of material bodies. Our judgment with respect to consciousness is based on the observation of external, material facts; from the outward behavior of another being, as compared with ourselves, we draw conclusions as to its immaterial inside. The conclusions are the more certain, the greater the similarity between ourselves and the other being. Therefore, about other humans we have no doubt that they are ruled by consciousnesses, or souls, similar to ours. Animals, even the lowest ones, have undoubtedly souls of their own and, if their mind differs from or seems inferior to ours, the elementary consciousness, the "I," should be exactly similar in its immaterial simplicity of pure existence. As to plants, opinions may differ; we simply do not know; analogy fails—and experiment is impossible—to prove or disprove the presence of consciousness in plants. Yet, in plants, as well as in animals, there is an organizing factor, a "subconscious consciousness," which seems to arrange and supervise their development in a purposeful, orderly manner, so different from the iron law of chance of the inorganic world. There may be immaterial mysteries beyond our reach in the world of atoms, too.

Finally, from an intuitive synthesis of our consciousness with that of others, and with the wonderful faculty of the cosmos to produce order, purpose and life from the apparent chaos of chance ruled by inflexible physical laws, we arrive at the belief in a Universal Consciousness, the Beginning and End of all things, the Primary and Ultimate Reality. Are the individual consciousnesses perhaps sparks, or atoms of the Universal Consciousness, separating from It for individual existence and returning to It at the end? The belief in a Superior Consciousness and in God, resulting from meditation and reasoning by analogy, is not less firmly founded than the belief in the similarity of the souls of fellow beings to ours. Who denies the existence of God, because He is the Unknowable, could with equal right consider himself alone in the universe and treat the rest as a dream. Scientific methods cannot prove the first, and they are equally unable to disprove the second standpoint. Our basic approach to the universe is through belief, even for a materialist; before studying the universe, we must believe that it exists outside the indubitable reality of our own consciousness.

31. Visiting Strange Worlds*
(A Glimpse of the Future)

1. IN THE OLD DAYS PEOPLE DID NOT TRUST TECHNICAL innovations. To convince them, one had to overcome the barrier of superstition and conservatism; many an innovator or inventor had to pay for his ideas with his life.

In modern times the situation has changed. The other extreme now prevails: the public is inclined to believe uncritically all kinds of technical possibilities, even when they are the product of pure fantasy. More critical circles, having been deceived by invented sensational stories, are often unable to distinguish between the possible and impossible. A new kind of distrust is growing which may become an obstacle to inventors, although they are no longer in danger of being burned at the stake.

This is just the present situation with respect to the possibility of interplanetary travel. Some kinds of space stories may have caused a certain negative reaction. Although there obviously exists a definite interest, some skeptical attitude can also be observed. Time and again the question is posed whether the possibility of interplanetary communication can be taken seriously at all.

* This chapter, written on the eve of the first artificial satellites, is reproduced here in its original version. The technical achievements of recent years, brilliant as they are, do not call for substantial alterations.

The present author was already occupied with these problems forty-six years ago. He laid down theoretically the general principles of space travel at a time when only one or two authors in the world were dealing with the subject, and when experiments in this field were non-existent. He did not publish his results, but, looking back now, he can state with satisfaction that there were no surprises in the ensuing developments. At present all the technical principles of space flight are, without exception, identical with those foreseen by the author almost half a century ago. This is mentioned here not because the author wants to claim credit for his foresight, but to show that the problem is theoretically not so complicated and depends much less on modern technical developments than do many other inventions, like radio, television, or color photography.

The conclusion is that space flight is certainly feasible, even with present technical means. The matter rests now with technical details and, of course, with finances, which represent the chief difficulty. One may guess that, with a few hundred million dollars properly spent, a flight to the moon and Mars (without landing, however) could be carried out, although a considerable time for preliminary experiments would be required, in addition to money.

The motive force in space is the rocket. Burning-hot gases, ejected backwards by the rocket, exert pressure in a direction opposite to their flow and push the space vehicle forward. In empty space a rocket would work even more efficiently than in air. However, the outflowing gases mean an enormous loss of materials; as a result, in a trip to the moon (without landing) the vehicle would spend 95 per cent of its mass in burned fuel, including containers thrown away, only 5 per cent remaining for the return journey.

Evidently, the vehicle must be built in several stages: the first stage of the size of an ocean liner, loaded with fuel to the extreme, carrying a second stage of smaller size, also crammed with fuel; the second stage carries a third, and so forth. When one stage of the vehicle has exhausted its fuel, it is abandoned and the next, smaller stage comes into action. The crew, of course, is confined to the last and smallest stage. Great velocities can

thus be built up in stages with ordinary chemical fuel
(i.e., without atomic energy), at the expense of a great,
progressive decimation of the apparatus. This means also
that a spaceship can be used for only one trip.

Landing is another problem. On the moon, where there
is no atmosphere, landing will have to be achieved by
reversing the rocket and using it as a brake; this is an
expensive method, wasteful of fuel. However, on returning to earth, or landing on Mars, the atmosphere of these
planets offers an opportunity of great material economy.
Landing in such a case will be made on the glider
principle, without using the fuel. The vehicle, with aeroplane wings of heat-resisting material, would glide hori-
zontally, circumnavigating the planet along the upper-
most atmospheric stratum until the velocity decreased
and landing became feasible. The principle is similar to
that of modern air liners, which have to cover a considerable distance on the airfield runway before stopping.
During gliding the crew of the spaceship must be insu-
lated from the outside heat of friction; their cabin will resemble a vacuum flask, inside which refrigerators will
keep the temperature down. The situation would be similar to that of the three righteous men of the Book of
Daniel who were placed in a fiery furnace.

Aeroplane wings could be used also for the take-off
from the earth or Mars, if coupled with the ram-jet principle. In this, the atmospheric air itself is used as part
of the material of the rocket. The open "mouth" of the
rocket swallows air while moving; this air, compressed
by the inertia of motion, enters a chamber where it is
heated by burning fuel, and then leaves the rocket
through a larger opening in the rear. Because of the
greater volume, the forward push of the outflowing hot
air exceeds the resistance of the cold air swallowed at
the front. A net forward impulse results. The ram jet
may lead to a considerable economy in fuel.

The problems of storage of oxygen for breathing, and
of food and drink, are no more complicated than in a
submarine. The conditions are to some extent even more
favorable, because solar radiation, always available in
interplanetary space, would supply energy for the chemical purification of used-up air, the growing of plants, and

the generation of rocket propulsion for steering purposes.

The absence of gravitation can be remedied by splitting the vehicle into two parts, connected by a chain, and by making these parts rotate around their common center of gravity with a suitable velocity. The centrifugal force generated in such a manner would replace gravitation. Owing to this "artificial gravitation," the inmates of the spaceship would be able to behave in the manner they were used to on earth. For example, they could pour and drink fluids without fearing that the contents would splash all over the compartment in a shower of drops; and they could lie in bed and sleep peacefully, without being sent to the "ceiling" at the slightest movement, the sleeper in one direction, the blanket, pillow and sheets in another. Then, there is the so-called danger of meteors, or the possibility of a collision with those little stony pellets which, moving with great speed, may pierce the walls of the vehicle. However, this danger is very much less than the chances of a traffic accident in our age of motorization. It is also possible to devise automatic protection against some consequences of a meteor hit, e.g., the leakage of air into space.

Notwithstanding all this, the technical difficulties to be overcome are enormous, before a living human penetrates into interplanetary space. The difficulties are, perhaps, as great as those which stood in the way of flying a century ago. The greatest obstacles are not of a mechanical but of a medical and psychological nature.

The fact that man has, after all, become master of flying despite the skeptical predictions of contemporaries, is a hopeful sign that one day he will also vanquish the intricacies of space travel. There can be little doubt about it, provided, of course, that humanity does not perish through its own foolishness before then.

2. Space stories are nowadays stepping into the place of the Wild West romance of half a century ago. "Space literature" has become an ingredient in the intellectual food of youth. This food is sometimes only a substitute, a kind of chewing gum for the brain. Yet it is the up-to-date response to the western spirit of adventure which in days past conquered the earth in search of new, strange lands. Now our planet has lost much of its

novelty and mystery; everything is known in its essentials, whereas the exploration of details does not appeal so much to the imagination. The adventurous young mind is turning to extraterrestrial worlds, expecting to find there the unusual which appears to have vanished from earth.

The play of fantasy in space fiction is ordinarily guided by the desire to have terrestrial heroes for actors; the physical conditions on other worlds are therefore pictured as being more similar to those on earth than they actually are. It may be pointed out that strange conditions can be found on earth, too—in the depths of the oceans, inside the rocky mantle of the earth's crust, or in the stratosphere. These differ from our habitual surroundings not more, perhaps, than the conditions on the surface of other planets. Yet very little fiction is concerned with these strange places of our own planet. The reason is obvious—the hero of a typical story of adventure, if transplanted to such places, would have to take so many precautions to protect his life that he would not be able to act in the expected way; he would be in the position of an experimental animal, used for scientific study and practically forbidden all activities which make up the spice of life. Space stories sometimes take advantage of the reader's ignorance of the actual conditions on other planets, and represent these conditions in a too favorable light.

On the moon and on Mars terrestrial visitors must be permanently enclosed in pressurized suits, carrying their oxygen supplies with them, in addition to water and food; no part of their body should be exposed, to avoid the deleterious effects of low pressure and ultraviolet light. Relaxation will be possible only inside the pressurized cabin of the spaceship, in which the problems of fresh air and cleanliness are extremely delicate and require close attention: full relaxation will be impossible. Personal relations between the members of the crew, enclosed for months or years in a narrow space, may easily become strained—a source of psychological dangers, not less menacing than the obvious physical dangers. The state of continuous alertness required by space travel can be compared to that of a soldier in front-line trenches, subject to continuous fire and gas attacks.

Under such conditions hardly any routine story of adventure or romance can develop. The whole trip will resemble more a laboratory experiment of long duration, involving dangers which only the foresight of a scientist can meet.

Also, ordinary terrestrial acts may lead to strange results. For example, a bucket of water emptied on the moon will instantly expand into a cloud of tiny icicles or snow, the vapor pressure first pulverizing the liquid into droplets or foam which then suddenly freezes, because of intense vaporization into the surrounding vacuum. The high lunar noon temperature, some 250°F, will not prevent this from happening. This might seem to be an easy method of making ice cream in the midst of the furnace of the lunar day.

3. Technically well-informed people hardly doubt that space travel will become a reality in the near future—say, within the next 20 to 100 years. The chemical energy of combustion of liquid fuel in oxygen, if used for rocket propulsion, is sufficient to carry the spaceship to the neighboring planets and back. Landing on planets surrounded by an atmosphere—Mars, Venus, and the earth itself—will not consume fuel, using the glider principle. The take-off from these planets is possible because their force of gravity is not excessive, whereas landing and take-off from the moon will consume comparatively little fuel. However, the cost of space trips will be enormous.

Atomic energy may help somewhat in solving the problem of space travel; but, in spite of the enormous amount of energy made available by fission of uranium, its application to rocket propulsion can only be very limited. The efficiency of the rocket depends solely on the velocity of the outflowing gases, and full use of atomic energy can be made only if this velocity is several hundred miles per second. In such a case the heating effect of the gases would be so great that the whole spaceship would be instantly annihilated by radiation.

Hence velocities of only a few miles per second are safely admissible, perhaps not more than the double of those attainable by chemical means. The advantages of atomic fuel are, therefore, greatly reduced, and in the centuries to come spaceships will probably prefer conventional chemical fuel.

All the above-mentioned circumstances set limitations to future space travel. In addition to visiting the nearest planets, it will be possible to approach Jupiter and circumnavigate it on a strongly elongated orbit; the round trip to Jupiter and back would take five years. One could also "land" there by gliding. However, as there is no land in the terrestrial sense—no solid surface except, perhaps, 35,000 miles underneath the visible exterior—the spaceship will be doomed to cruise continually inside Jupiter's atmosphere, which will be possible only with the aid of atomic fuel. Without atomic power there will be no hope of getting out and back to earth. An atomic spaceship performing as a ram jet could rise to the top of Jupiter's atmosphere and, with a last effort, transfer itself to a circular orbit, becoming a tiny satellite of the giant planet. From there the crew would convey to earth, by light or radio signals, the experience gained inside Jupiter's atmosphere. The next step—the return to earth—would be fantastically difficult. To overcome Jupiter's gravitation, the spaceship must swing itself into an elongated orbit which finally opens the way homewards; for this purpose the ship must acquire an additional velocity of about 12 miles per second. This is a somewhat greater effort than that required to overcome terrestrial gravitation. With the depleted stores and shrunken size of the ship the task appears to be almost impossible. Even with 4 miles per second as the velocity of the rocket exhaust gases, attainable only with the aid of atomic energy, the mass of material (gases) fired out to space by the rocket must be 20 times that of the remaining apparatus. If this latter is assumed to weigh 100 tons (minimum for an atomic plant), the ship starting from Jupiter should weigh 2,000 tons, and that which originally started from earth 50,000 tons at least. For conventional fuel the figures would be: final weight at return 10 tons; starting weight from Jupiter 4,000 tons; starting from earth 1.6 million tons. For a small spaceship there is no return: the trip to Jupiter will be a one-way journey.

The reward for the perilous and expensive voyage may be more knowledge about the laws of life. We know that the conditions on Jupiter are prohibitive as far as terrestrial forms of life are concerned. The atmosphere there contains ammonia and methane, but no oxygen, and is therefore poisonous by our standards. But it is not impossible that other forms of life can adapt themselves to Jupiter's conditions. Although extremely cold at the top of the atmosphere, the temperature on Jupiter at a depth where the pressure is some 50 atmospheres may be equal to that of the earth's surface; dim light will penetrate to this depth, especially through the breaks between clouds, which are known as the dark bands of the planet. Conditions for primitive organisms suspended in the thick atmosphere and, perhaps, for strange higher forms of life, may exist there—all floating in the "air" like marine organisms in water.

4. We have outlined the physiological, psychological, and technical difficulties of space travel. The difficulties are formidable, but not insuperable; nevertheless, it is clear that, for a long time to come, space travel will serve purely scientific purposes, pursued by small crews of self-sacrificing scientists and explorers.

Another aspect of space travel has been widely discussed, although not always in a sufficiently realistic perspective: that of the colonization of other worlds. It is argued, and quite rightly, that with the progress of civilization on earth, shortage of space and food may ensue. Populations multiply in a geometrical progression and, however slow the actual rate of increase, after a sufficient lapse of time—be it 200, 1,000 or 10,000 years—famine will put a ceiling to it, unless humanity reverts to barbarous and uncivilized methods of destruction (ordinary wars do not seem to have any effect). No controls will be efficient, because those genetic strains which defy the controls will multiply at the expense of others. Those who deny these prospects are closing their eyes to implacable biological and arithmetical laws.

An alternative is colonization of space, but only if it can be achieved on an unlimited scale. With the technical means which we can foresee at present, the cost of transport of one settler to the moon would run into millions of dollars; clearly, no mass colonization can be practicable under such circumstances. As a last resort before emigration to the moon becomes a necessity, humanity has first to make habitable all the barren areas of dry land—deserts, mountains, and tundras—and even to cover the oceans with gigantic rafts where cities can be built and crops grown. Climate has to be controlled for this purpose, but this would be child's play as compared with space colonization: the basic materials—air and water—are plentiful on earth, whereas in space they have to be imported or manufactured. Even underground cities and farms, artificially illuminated and hewn out of solid rock, are more feasible than settlements in space.

Colonization of space would require at least a thousand times greater productivity in machine building than is now attainable. Machines that build greater machines, robots producing robots, seems to be the solution. Muscular manpower will lose its importance except, perhaps, in sport.

The outlook may or may not seem to be dull but—who knows?—after thousands of years, when such advanced technique will be possible, man may find unheard-of ways of making life interesting and beautiful. Indeed, unless this is achieved, the danger of self-destruction will loom over a humanity oppressed by boredom and lack of purpose.

Epilogue

LIFE IS BRIEF AND ENDS IN THE UNKNOWN. THE WHOLE life of humanity is but a moment of the cosmic time scale, and we know that despite all efforts toward self-preservation, mankind will vanish eventually. Maybe there will be a successor to it on earth, maybe not. Yet we can firmly believe that there are elsewhere others of our semblance, some very much farther advanced on the track of evolution.

The whole cosmos is performing a giant oscillation. At present it expands, shot out of the chaos of the primeval focal point and, while in flight, sheltering the wondrous metamorphoses of life. After many thousands of millions of years, expansion will cease, and the world will collapse into its former focus, the primeval atom, where material individuality will melt and disappear; only to rebound and precipitate itself into new expansion, creating new worlds, with new metamorphoses and dreams.

Material things are born, vanish, and are born again. This is the rhythm of the physical world. All that can be measured, weighed, and timed obeys the rhythm.

Yet there is something in us which has neither measure, weight, nor time: our consciousness, the "I," individually different from, yet similar to other "I's." Is it not a droplet or atom of the Great Cosmic Consciousness? The first reality of our knowledge, the only existence of which we have no doubt, our only gate and window through which we perceive the world . . . does it upon death rejoin the Great Consciousness? Or does it remain an atom by itself, to awaken elsewhere with the same feeling of identity and individuality? Being outside space and time, time intervals would not matter to it; when awakening somewhere after billions of billions of great cosmic oscillations, would it not be filled with the same fresh sense of individuality that it has now, or had billions of cosmic oscillations before our time?

Maybe this consciousness is only the superficies of subconscious depths reaching to the root of all things. Maybe there is analogy with chemical affinity, an element of consciousness (or soul) combining with a suitable organism. If consciousness is outside time and space, temporal or spatial barriers would here be of no avail.

Only from such a standpoint would it not seem strange and unbelievable that we exist. Our earthly life is but a moment in eternity; the chances of its lasting at this moment, our "present," are infinitesimally small as compared with the chances of its no longer, or not yet, being there. If transient and unrepeatable, our present individual consciousness would be an extraordinarily improbable phenomenon.

All this sounds irrational. Yet modern science also arrives at irrationality in the study of the material world. This is, for example, the case with wave mechanics; it deals especially with atomic physics, but actually embraces all physics, to some extent even biology. This discipline is based on the irrational assertion that each elementary particle is at the same time a wave, and vice versa.

Of course, we do not know the answer to the riddle.

Nescimus! Yet it would be foolish to assume that only what we already know exists. Inquisitiveness of the human mind has revealed many great mysteries; greater mysteries are to be disclosed in the future; yet the greatest mystery of the cosmos may remain hidden from us forever.

Index